Are you eating an orange?

and other stories from the Autistic Spectrum

for Daniel
Enjoy!

Debi x

For everyone on the spectrum out there, diagnosed or otherwise, and for anyone who walks to a different beat.

Are you eating an orange?

and other stories from the Autistic Spectrum

Debi Brown

Aspiedebi Publications

First published in the United Kingdom in 2010
by Aspiedebi Publications.

A CIP catalogue record for this book
is available from the British Library

ISBN: 978-0-9566649-0-7

The author is grateful to Alex Plötz and Christopher Mountford for permission to reproduce photographs.

Disclaimer
The author does not take responsibility for any decision taken as a result of the information contained in this book. The author does not endorse, approve of or assume responsibility for any product, brand or company. None of the information contained in this book is designed to be taken as medical advice. Always consult a qualified medical practitioner before implementing any dietary intervention.

Always remember,
different is cool.

Luke Jackson, aspie

Contents

Acknowledgements

Everyone is effectively a sum of all the effort and time put into them by everyone else in their lives. No-one is an island and no-one gets where they are on their own. It is therefore impossible to acknowledge everyone who has helped me in my life. However, I need to give my immense thanks to a few people in particular:

To my parents, for doing the best that they possibly could and for giving me early intervention, even if they did not realise it.

To all my friends and the staff at ARC, for being amazing.

To Jamie Allan and family, for liking me just as I am.

To Fiona Merriweather, for being a pure ray of sunshine and love and for helping me get de-freaked out after my diagnosis.

To Barbara Harrington, for all her wisdom and goodness.

To Sinead Feeney, for being outstanding in a million ways.

To Charlene Tait, for reading my 23,000 word essays (which were just a wee bit over the word limit!).

To Annie Swan and Jenni Higgs, for teaching me it was okay to be an aspie.

To Norman Green, Richard Anderson, Ian Brooke, Harry Campbell and Alison Briers for their help with the text of this book.

To Christopher Mountford, Richard Anderson, Daniel Oi and David Stevenson for their help with various computer things to do with this book.

To Alison Briers and Elizabeth Finnen, for help beyond the call of duty.

To my present and past employers and work colleagues who, through mutual misunderstandings as well as kindnesses, have taught me a lot about the NT world.

To my very clever and brilliant Neurotypical friends, who have helped explain parts of the NT world to me.

To all the kids and volunteers at SNAC at QP, who make me feel so incredibly accepted and with whom I have a wonderful time.

To Mark Allan, Megan McIver and Emily McDonald - I love playing with you.

To Luke Jackson, Jacqui Jackson, Liane Holliday Willey, Wendy Lawson, Olga Bogdashina and Marilyn Le Breton, who have all taught me a lot through their own brilliant books.

To Ian Jordan, for all his encouragement, practical help and for everything that he does for people on the spectrum.

Foreword

Sometimes there is need for a person to see beyond what is current knowledge and question the way professionals work by using a new paradigm. Debi has used her experience in determining what has been beneficial in her aspie journey, she has distilled this knowledge and produced an extraordinary book that will provide hope, enlightenment and understanding of how a person can rise above their difficulties using a variety of non-standard interventions.

Everyone on the autistic spectrum (and their families) should read this book and become aware. It just might change your life.

Be inspired.

Ian Jordan

Introduction

Hello and welcome to my book and the colourful world of the autistic spectrum. If you are on the spectrum yourself, you are especially welcome.

I am an aspie (person with Asperger Syndrome) and I got my informal diagnosis about three years ago. Since then, I have found learning about the autistic spectrum to be really fascinating; particularly, seeing how various things matched up and explained bits of my life. However, it also upset me a lot at first. There is a lot written about the autistic spectrum in terms such as "the Triad of Impairments" and "severe impairment in social interaction". This kind of description makes me feel very hopeless and causes "unnecessary suffering", so-called because this suffering is not caused by the Autism itself; only by prejudices and overly-negative descriptions. The good news is that we are not the stereotypes that society in general thinks we are, and many things are possible.

There is also a lot of good stuff written about the spectrum, which nourishes self-esteem and encourages growth, but it takes a lot of reading through the awful stuff to find it. This negative stuff can be very damaging to self-esteem, particularly in the fragile period directly following diagnosis. Hence, the purpose of this book is to add something to the "good side" of the scales, so that for people who get diagnosed in the future, the ratio of helpful to depressing literature will be increased, even just by one. I will also reference many of the good materials that I have found, which you might like to look at too.

Also, the more I learn about Autism, the more I am coming to the opinion that the real experts at the moment are not the professionals in the field. The most useful things I have found are generally not officially sanctioned at all. Three examples are the Gluten-Free, Casein-Free (GF-CF) Diet, the Alexander Technique, and glasses with coloured lenses. In the case of the Gluten-Free, Casein-Free

Are you eating an orange?

Diet, it is claimed there is not sufficient evidence to recommend this. However, an awful lot of autistic folk and parents of autistic children have tried it and found that it works. The Alexander Technique has been around for about one hundred years, but I have not been able to find any scientific research supporting the use of the Alexander Technique for autistic people. I will explain to you in this book why I think it works, given what I know about Autism, what I know about the Alexander Technique and my personal experience. In the case of glasses with coloured lenses, this field is so new and unexplored, most people do not even know about it, let alone having done the required research before this can be an official recommendation.

The great shame about this, is people who only go to the official sources will not get the right kind of help, until the Autism field has advanced quite considerably. And we need the right help *now*, not in fifty years time when someone might possibly, if they can find the time/money/inclination, have conducted the required trials. It is one of those things where if you or your parent(s) are bright enough, interested enough, curious enough, brave enough to go against doctors' recommendations, have the time and inclination and if you are not in denial about being autistic in the first place, you can do sufficient research and find lots of things that help. However, if you are not *all* of the above, the Autism field in general may fail you. For example, many adults on the spectrum are on some kind of medication, typically for anxiety, depression or for stomach problems, and at least some people will be suffering quite serious side effects from the medication. However, most adults are not on the Gluten-Free, Casein-Free Diet, which might well help some or all of their stomach problems. And, if you read the statistics about how many people are completely friendless, unemployed, living with their parents well into adulthood and who receive no or very little support from the system, is it surprising that mental health problems result? In my opinion, in many cases, it may simply be life management that has to be sorted out, rather than a problem that needs to be treated with medication. This is also where this book might help. It is completely unofficial and contains many controversial opinions, but I hope it will provide some useful signposts to others wandering in the fog, particularly in areas where the professionals just do not know. In fact, some of these theories are so controversial that some of my friends now think I am off my rocker. However, my advice is try things for yourself, otherwise you will never know. I am definitely not encouraging you to blindly follow my advice or anyone else's. But what I would say, is not to fail to try something, just because social workers, doctors, teachers and the National Autistic Society have not recommended it to you. Try it. If it does not work, you can stop it. If it does, great, continue.

So, this book is part autobiographical, part experimentalist guide book and part text book, including an inside-out explanation of living on the autistic spectrum and what that means to me. Also, although I am speaking mainly from my own experiences, I have done a lot of reading, I have studied Autism at University, I do various bits of volunteering with people on the spectrum and I have quite a few autistic friends, who I have met through University, work, friendships and hobbies. Since like attracts like, I reckon I may know more people on the spectrum than most people would. Knowing other folk on the spectrum enriches my experience and understanding.

A note about terminology

Throughout this book, I will use the term "autistic" to refer to anyone on the autistic spectrum, and not (unless otherwise specified) to mean someone with Kanner's Autism as opposed to Asperger Syndrome (AS).

I will use "aspie" (a term coined by Liane Holliday Willey) to refer to someone who has Asperger Syndrome. For consistency, and to avoid confusion with the entire autistic spectrum, I will therefore use "autie" to refer to people who have Kanner's Autism/

Are you eating an orange?

Childhood Autism. I will use Neurotypical (NT) to mean someone who is not on the autistic spectrum.

Liane Holliday Willey likes "aspie" because it means neither referring to yourself by reference to a man (Asperger was male), or by reference to a syndrome. I use "aspie" in the same way as Liane, with the same intentions, and not because I am trying to offend anyone who has a different view on this word. A further reason that I prefer the term "aspie" is that "person with AS" implies that there is a fully normal person in there somewhere, if one could only extract that darned AS from the person. Whereas actually, Autism is integrally woven into the fabric of our being; you cannot separate that from our personality, and many of us would not want you to, even if you could. If you could take away my Autism, you would not get me; you would get a completely different human being.

Sola Shelly makes a really good point on this subject: "Just like you won't call me a person with womanhood, I don't want to be called a person with Asperger Syndrome. I am an Aspie." (Shelly, 2004, p. 6). I wholeheartedly agree!

I have tried hard to make this book as honest as possible and the best it could possibly be. I hope it will be helpful to you on your journey.

What are Autism and Asperger Syndrome?

Okay, so, I have a diagnosis. Perhaps you do too. So what are Autism and Asperger Syndrome?

This is not a text book exactly and there will be many other sources of this kind of information. However, for completeness and for readers new to the concept of the autistic spectrum, I will begin with a very brief history and description of the spectrum.

Leo Kanner

Leo Kanner studied eleven children and wrote the first paper on what he termed "early infantile Autism" (Kanner, 1943). Kanner noted several key traits, including:

- innate inability to form the usual affective contact with other people;
- intense insistence on sameness in their routines;
- extreme aloneness;
- failure to use language to convey meaning;
- muteness or marked abnormality of speech;
- fascination with and dexterity in manipulating objects;
- attractive, alert, intelligent appearance.

Later, Kanner suggested the criteria sufficient for diagnosis were the first two of the above list. (Wing, 1996).

Kanner's children also had particular strengths, such as a surprisingly good vocabulary, excellent memory and visual-spatial skills, strong interest in numbers and letters and often precocious literacy. Kanner described them as potentially very able. The children had strange and intense anxieties, other mood issues and odd eating patterns. The only physical difference Kanner noted was that about half of the children had unusually large head circumferences.

Are you eating an orange?

Some of the children's parents and siblings also shared the unusual features of Kanner's children. However, Kanner found the condition was present from "the very beginning of life", unlike schizophrenia, and hence concluded their upbringing could not be entirely to blame.

Hans Asperger

In 1944, independently of Kanner, Hans Asperger published a paper about behaviour in older children and adolescents (Wing, 1997).

Asperger's key features included:

- naïve, inappropriate, social approaches to others;
- intense circumscribed interest in particular subjects, for example, railway timetables;
- good grammar and vocabulary but monotonous speech used for monologues, not two-way conversation;
- poor motor coordination;
- level of ability in the borderline, average or superior range, but often with specific learning difficulties in one or two subjects;
- a marked lack of common sense; and
- poor intonation and body language.

The parents did not observe any abnormality until after three years of age, or when the children started school (Wing, 1996).

The Autistic Spectrum

Lorna Wing and Judith Gould (1970s) carried out a study in which they examined all children under fifteen in the Camberwell area of London who had any kind of physical or learning disability or abnormality of behaviour (Wing, 1996). They concluded that Kanner's Autism and Asperger Syndrome were both part of a wider spectrum of autistic conditions, whereas both Asperger and Kanner had believed their conditions to be unique (Wing, 1997). This study also led Wing and Gould to define the "Triad of Impairments" (see below).

There are quite a few different estimates of how many people are on the autistic spectrum. The figure the National Autistic Society presently uses is one percent of the population. That is an awful lot of people! The number of people being diagnosed is increasing; however, it is not known whether this is due to an increase in the actual autistic population, or whether this is due to increased public awareness and improvements in diagnosing more of us.

Current diagnostic criteria for Autism and AS

The current diagnostic criteria are defined in the International Statistical Classification of Diseases and Related Health problems, tenth edition of the World Health Organisation (ICD-10, 1994), and the Diagnostic and Statistical Manual, fourth edition (DSM-IV) of the American Psychiatric Association (American Psychiatric Association, 1994). ICD-10 is the system of classification of diseases in Europe whilst DSM-IV is the US equivalent. I hate the fact that Autism sits in there as a "disease", but that is unfortunately the case.

According to both ICD-10 and DSM-IV, Kanner's Autism (otherwise known as Childhood Autism) is diagnosed in people who have impairments in the following three areas:

- Communication
- Social Interaction
- Imagination

These three areas are known as "The Triad of Impairments". This is another nasty term, but do not worry, I will not be using it very much in this book.

Are you eating an orange?

The communication impairment is not in the diagnostic criteria for Asperger Syndrome, but the other two impairments must be found. For AS, there must also be no clinically significant general delay in spoken or receptive language or cognitive development. Also, for a diagnosis of AS, self-help skills, adaptive behaviour and curiosity about the environment should be consistent with normal intellectual development during the first three years of life.

Despite unusual sensory perception and experiences being very widely reported by people on the spectrum and their relatives, the presence of such sensory issues is not included in the diagnostic criteria. Hence, the presence or absence of noticeable sensory issues does not affect whether a diagnosis is given.

Sub-categories of the autistic spectrum

The autistic spectrum includes the following:

- Kanner's Autism
    - Low Functioning
    - High Functioning
- Asperger Syndrome
- Rett Syndrome
- Childhood Disintegrative Disorder
- Pervasive Developmental Disorder Not Otherwise Specified (PDD-NOS)

This book mainly concerns Kanner's Autism and Asperger Syndrome.

As indicated above, Kanner's Autism is itself informally sub-categorised into two groups: low functioning and high functioning. These terms are not in the diagnostic criteria, but I believe the dividing line often used is whether the person eventually learns to talk or not. Aspies, by definition, do talk because they have no clinically significant delay in spoken or receptive language, so there is no sub-categorising of the Asperger population into low and high functioning.

Autism vs. Asperger Syndrome

Even though Kanner's Autism and Asperger Syndrome are defined separately in both ICD-10 and DSM-IV, many people now believe that this distinction is artificial and in reality, there is no distinction between aspies and auties.

Although according to ICD-10, for Asperger Syndrome, there is no requirement for any communication impairment, I have heard professionals remark that they have never actually met any aspie who does *not* have some kind of impairment in communication.

Moreover, although AS is ruled out in the presence of a clinically significant delay in language, Howlin (2003) challenges the assumption that early language development in Asperger Syndrome is essentially normal. In contrast, she found that in adult aspies, the level of language and the social use of language is often "markedly impaired".

Howlin's test results did not support the view that High Functioning Autism and Asperger Syndrome are distinct conditions, and instead highlighted the lack of any substantial difference between the two diagnostic groups in adulthood (Howlin, 2003). She concluded that any distinctions that do exist in early childhood may become less marked with age.

From the diagnostic criteria, given that it seems that in reality, all aspies do have a communication impairment, it seems to me that the main difference between Kanner's Autism and Asperger Syndrome is whether there was a clinically significant general delay in spoken or receptive language or cognitive development, evidenced in early childhood. If there was, this rules out Aspergers, leaving Autism the main alternative possibility. The presence or absence of a language delay was also how Howlin made her distinction between the two groups (Howlin, 2003). Importantly, she did not apply the DSM-IV diagnostic criteria strictly in respect of Aspergers, because of being able to identify so few cases from the patient database who met the strict criteria.

My personal conclusion from all this is that the presence or absence of an early language delay is a bizarre way of differentiating between Autism and AS in adults. I do not think it is very relevant to the present stage of development of a thirty-year old whether they started speaking at fourteen months or two and a half years old. Even if their talking was a bit late, they are likely to have caught up a long way before the age of thirty. Therefore, it is very difficult to put adults in the correct group. It is perhaps for this reason that many studies have not been able to find any differences between aspies and high functioning autie adults.

Like Howlin (2003), I am not convinced there is actually any difference between Autism and AS. I apparently officially have Autism, as opposed to AS, although I cannot see any real differences between me and the aspies I have met. I learned to talk at age two and did not previously do any communicative babbling, so this is not essentially normal language development and is indicative of a delay, but it is not a huge delay in the grand scheme of things. Other auties for instance, might begin to talk at age five, or age eight. When I compare myself to some auties, I can see that we share all of the same issues, just with differing severity. It is like taking a magnifying glass to myself. When I compare myself to aspies, I seem to be more high functioning and have less significant sensory issues than some. So, understanding where I fit in the spectrum is very confusing for me. Intuitively, the aspie group is where I classified myself, before I got a formal diagnosis of Autism. I am coming to the conclusion that it is all one continuum, and that a division between Autism and AS is not very helpful. In society, aspies can be disadvantaged because of the perceived "mildness" of their condition compared to Autism, and this is completely wrong. It also seems probable to me that some people who have a diagnosis of Aspergers can be more severely affected than some people who have a diagnosis of Autism.

How can you tell if you have these impairments or not?

Before my official diagnosis, after reading that Autism is defined by the Triad of Impairments, I found it very difficult to judge whether I personally had these impairments. How should I know if I have an impairment in imagination? I have never lived in someone else's head. So, if you too are not sure if this applies to you, then read on!

In looking for further clarification, I found the following list of characteristics under "Asperger Syndrome" on Wikipedia, which I found much more helpful:

1.	Difficulty reading the social and emotional messages in the eyes. People with AS do not look at eyes often, and when they do, they cannot read them.

2.	Making literal interpretations. AS individuals have trouble interpreting colloquialisms, sarcasm, and metaphors.

3.	Being considered disrespectful and rude. Prone to egocentric behaviour, individuals with Aspergers miss cues and warning signs that this behaviour is inappropriate.

4.	Honesty and deception. Children with Aspergers are often considered "too honest" and have difficulty being deceptive, even at the expense of hurting someone's feelings.

5.	Becoming aware of making social errors. As children with Aspergers mature and become aware of their mind blindness, their fear of making a social mistake, and their self-criticism when they do so, can lead to social phobia.

6.   A sense of paranoia. Because of their mind blindness, persons with Aspergers have trouble distinguishing the difference between the deliberate or accidental actions of others, which can in turn lead to a feeling of paranoia.

7.   Managing conflict. Being unable to understand other points of view can lead to inflexibility and an inability to negotiate conflict resolution. Once the conflict is resolved, remorse may not be evident.

8.   Awareness of hurting the feelings of others. A lack of empathy often leads to unintentionally offensive or insensitive behaviours.

9.   Repairing someone's feelings. Lacking intuition about the feelings of others, people with AS have little understanding of how to console someone or how to make them feel better.

10.   Recognizing signs of boredom. Inability to understand other people's interests can lead AS persons to be inattentive to others. Conversely, people with AS often fail to notice when others are uninterested.

11.   Introspection and self-consciousness. Individuals with AS have difficulty understanding their own feelings or their impact on the feelings of other people.

12.   Clothing and person hygiene. People with AS tend to be less affected by peer pressure than others. As a result, they often do what is comfortable and are unconcerned about their impact on others.

13.   Reciprocal love and grief. Since people with AS react more practically than emotionally, their expressions of affection and grief are often short and weak.

14.   Understanding of embarrassment and faux pas. Although persons with AS have an intellectual understanding of embarrassment and faux pas, they are unable to grasp concepts on an emotional level.

15.   Coping with criticism. People with AS are compelled to correct mistakes, even when they are made by someone in a position of authority, such as a teacher. For this reason, they can be unwittingly offensive.

16.   Speed and quality of social processing. Because they respond through reasoning and not intuition, AS individuals tend to process social information more slowly than the norm, leading to uncomfortable pauses or delays in response.

17.   Exhaustion. As people with AS begin to understand Theory of Mind, they must make a deliberate effort to process social information. This often leads to mental exhaustion.

(Attwood, T., cited in http://en.wikipedia.org/wiki/Asperger_ Syndrome, accessed on 20 February 2007.)

As soon as I read this, I reckoned that the vast majority of these points were true for me and I had no doubt from that moment on that I was on the autistic spectrum.

If you are still not sure, another source of information that could help you decide whether you might be on the spectrum is "The Adult Autism Spectrum Quotient (AQ test)", which was developed by the Autism Research Centre at the University of Cambridge. This can be found on the internet (see Recommended Reading).

My definition of Autism

You may have already gathered that I really do not like how Autism is defined by a whole list of negative characteristics.

Are you eating an orange?

Indeed, one of the main aims of this book is to present Autism in a much more positive light. The "Triad of Impairments" definition is no use if we want to keep our self-esteem intact. Besides which, it only really begins to scratch the surface. So, I will give you my definition instead.

Autism is a different way of thinking and being, characterised in seeing the details rather than the big picture and in that social concerns are not the most important thing for us. Being autistic is not better, and is not worse than being Neurotypical; being autistic is just different and that is okay. Autism is also no-one's fault.

Autism means liking structure, routines and predictability rather than spontaneity. It means doing things properly. It means being more interested in *being* good rather than *seeming* to be good. It means honesty and integrity. It means being direct rather than indirect. It means basing decisions on logic rather than on emotions. It means being unique rather than being a sheep. It means passion and commitment. It means having an intense focus on one's interests. It means that your prime motivation in making choices is not what other people will think. It means being literal, loyal and straight-forward. It means having a good memory, but being less able to work things out. It means having a brain that gets over-loaded easily through trying to process every single detail rather than filtering out the important stuff and only processing that. It means difficulty with generalising from one situation to the next.

Autism also means having a body that works in a different way to other people's bodies. Although I am not a doctor and so cannot speak with authority on this subject, I have formed some personal beliefs and opinions about this. There are two main body systems I believe to be different, but there may be more. The first is the sensory processing system. I believe that sensory processing of all the senses is affected, in most people and possibly everyone on the spectrum. Sensory input may be too loud or too soft on each of the different channels or it may vary between the two. Only one channel of information may be processed at once, leading to time delays between different sensory systems. The second system I believe to be affected is the digestive system. Although I do not know whether this is true for everyone, I think that autistic people are likely to be intolerant to gluten and casein, and may have leaky gut syndrome. There can be problems with diarrhoea, constipation and weight loss/gain. Also, in people who are affected like this, I think that the immune system may be overloaded if gluten and casein are included in the diet, causing a reduced resistance to colds, flus and other illnesses. I will talk more about the sensory system and digestive system later in this book.

Autism means communication difficulties with some Neurotypical people, not necessarily because you have poor communication skills, but because they themselves are completely different to you and are likely to be ignorant about Autism. Being autistic means needing a tolerant society, and until that happens, it means seeking out and collecting a bunch of people who can understand you.

Autism means trying things that society recommends, but with an awareness that what works for Neurotypical people does not necessarily work for you.

Life-story and Diagnosis

I floated around most of my adult life being totally unaware of my fundamental aspie-ness. I went to a main-stream school, studied physics at university and I have had various office-based jobs. To my horror, I found out that I was on the spectrum quite recently, when a friend said she thought I was autistic. One hour of internet-research later, I knew it was true. Whereas the previous day, I had thought I was completely normal, suddenly, I have a syndrome. Lovely. So how did this happen? Well…

In childhood, I was shy and anxious. I hated transitions, such as starting primary school, and moving up from primary to secondary school. When a change had to happen, I was usually not ready for it and did not want it. If there had been the option to remain a child and not grow up, I would have definitely taken it. I considered the job of being an adult, and there seemed little to recommend it. Particularly, being a parent seemed like enforced slavery, and I wondered why people did it. There did not seem to be any benefit to compensate for having to have a job, housework and child-rearing.

School was sometimes difficult, but home was nice and safe. At home, I enjoyed playing in the garden, doing handstands, cartwheels and forward rolls in the garden, playing with lego, lying in the grass and looking at the clouds, and stroking every passing cat.

One of my earliest memories is a new girl joining my class a few months after I had started in primary school. The teacher told me that this new girl wanted to be my friend. I remember feeling rather surprised (why would she want me to be her friend?), but I was agreeable and went along with it. It has only recently been explained to me that five year olds do not generally enter a class and single out who they want as a friend and that I was most likely sitting by myself, not interacting, so the teacher artificially created

26

me a friend. I was shocked to learn this, as I take what people say at face value and I had never questioned my teacher's statement. I know she acted with the best intentions, but I feel like I was lied to.

I remember being nervous about going to children's birthday parties and about going to my friend's house. My parents normally made me go, and reminded me that I normally enjoyed it once I got there. Once, I was invited to go swimming with my friend. My Mum, having heard me stress about going there before, invented an excuse that I could not go because we were visiting our cousins that afternoon. I was horrified that my Mum, who was good and perfect, had done such an immoral thing as lying. However, even worse was the fact that my Mum explained to me that I was going to have to continue the lie, if my friend's family asked me about that. I was horrified that I was going to be forced to lie too. In the end, I did have to lie to the family, and I did that very badly, by being monosyllabic and not looking at anyone. Luckily for me, they did not probe very hard for details. My morals about such things have relaxed a lot since then, but as a child, I felt very bad about such things.

I was definitely delayed in some areas. For example, one of my friends now has a two-year old daughter who likes pretend play such as tea parties. As a child, I never did this. Even now, as an adult, although I know the purpose of pretend play is practice for being an adult, even so, it seems a very bizarre thing to be doing. The other day, I saw a four-year-old on a train, pretending to be using a plastic mobile phone. These activities fascinate me, because I wonder why on earth these children are doing such things, which have and had no interest for me at all. This makes me quite sure that I never played in this way as a child.

I was still happily watching children's TV when going into my teenage years, which caused my Dad some concern, and in my last year of junior school, I suddenly ran into lots of social difficulties. My friend (who had lasted all the way from primary school) grew up and I did not. She basically outgrew me and found other friends. I started playing with younger children instead of with my age group. The teachers told me this was not socially acceptable and were concerned about my transition to secondary school.

My parents encouraged me to do lots of activities, so I was very busy. I learned the flute and piano and got up to grade eight standard (the top grade) in both. My Mum was a music teacher and was passionate about music. I never liked music practice, but Mum said I would be grateful when I was older. I was given the chance to quit when I got to grade five on each instrument. However, I was then told "it is a shame to give up now you've got so far" and I did enjoy the recognition I got from other people through being thought to be good at something, although I still was not actually enjoying the music itself. My music teacher at school, on hearing me play, thought that it was strange because I was playing the right notes but it was as if I was not actually hearing the music that I was playing. This is probably very close to the truth; because I only properly process one channel of sensory information at once, I probably was not able to listen at the same time as play the music. From music practice, I learned to be hard-working and diligent and that I could achieve things if I tried hard. However, I also learned that my feelings (not liking the music practice or getting anything out of it) were irrelevant and that I should continue to work hard. Even now, I sometimes ignore what I feel about something and carry on doing it despite not enjoying it. This is a bit of a problem in adult life. I sometimes do things because I feel "I should" or "I have to" regardless of how I feel.

I also did ballet, tap and jazz dancing, which I did enjoy. I liked the act of movement, and though I was rather stiff and not naturally elegant, by intelligence, I managed to achieve a fairly high standard.

At age thirteen, I discovered trampolining, which became my all-consuming interest for the next seven years. I still do not really understand why everyone in the world does not want to trampoline. It is the closest thing to flying that I have experienced and is simply wonderful. Now, I realise I like trampolining so much because of my hyposensitivity to the vestibular sensory system - it is a pure movement thing. I got quite good at trampolining; beyond the teaching of my school games teacher anyway, and then I pestered my Dad to drive me to a proper trampoline club in a neighbouring town. I learned front somersaults, tucked and piked, front somersaults with half twist out, back somersaults, tucked, piked and straight, three-quarter front somersaults, three-quarter back somersaults, that kind of thing. However, I did not get much further than this. I was not brilliant at twisting and the higher level skills tended to combine twisting motions with somersaulting motions. This required a high level of spatial awareness; the timing is critical and it is vital to know when to open out of a somersault/start a twisting motion. However, I had big problems with not being able to use visual clues whilst in the air. I now know this is because I was only using one sensory channel at once (monoprocessing). When trampolining, I mostly used my vestibular system to tell me where I was in the air and which way up I was at any given moment. I would be told to look out for a certain feature on the sports hall roof half way through a somersault, to tell me when to kick out, or twist. However, I could not also use my eyes at the same time as the vestibular sense. This ended up feeling quite dangerous and I got to a point where I did not feel I could safely progress anymore due to my processing difficulties.

Secondary school was a bit of a miserable time; not fitting in, sometimes getting bullied but more often just excluded. I emerged from secondary school with very low self-confidence. In terms of autistic behaviour, a lot of my behaviour at school was very passive. However, being involved in so many music/dance/trampolining activities made up for not having a social life. I was a pretty busy child/teenager.

Are you eating an orange?

Things went a lot better at university. I really enjoyed my first year at University and gained a lot of confidence from living away from home. I met some really nice friends and felt properly included. I also started doing quite a lot of choir singing and found I was really good at that. Despite this, I was still sticking to my passive-type behaviour of being quiet, shy and retiring. In the summer holiday between first and second year, I went with a friend to work as a waitress in the kitchens of a summer camp in America. I have to say, that was pretty disastrous! I tried really hard, but I was quite bad at it. Luckily for me, the tasks were at least quite repetitive, but my executive functioning abilities were not quite up to scratch. I would begin one task (such as sweeping) and then think "oooh whilst I am here, I'll tidy a couple of tables", and then I would forget to finish the sweeping, and it annoyed the other waitresses that I did not always finish what I had started. They tended to order me about, which I did not like. I felt completely socially incapable of relating to these other girls at all. They were like aliens to me. They were interested in boys, hair, fashion, pop music, magazines, and I did not have a clue what to talk to them about. One of the girls was nice to me at first, but then accused me of copying my friend's behaviour and not having a personality of my own, or something along these lines. This was probably a pretty fair comment – I was probably copying my friend's behaviour as a model of how to act. However, this girl then stopped being nice to me and did not really talk to me again, which seemed a bit harsh.

The unexpected upshot of having had a fairly difficult and sometimes miserable summer was that I was so pleased and relieved to be back at University, with my friends who tended to be fellow physics-geeks and other nice people, that I stopped being shy and retiring and started to talk! To my surprise, I found that I was not snubbed, and that people might laugh at what I said, or how I said it, but they were laughing in a nice way and were still my friends. So, at this point, a lot of my behaviour changed from "passive" to "active-but-odd". I do not think there is an option to be autistic and "active but not odd" because however skilled one is, one cannot avoid coming across as a bit eccentric/odd/plain weird. So, the best we can do is be bravely odd and proud of it.

After University, I have had a number of office-based jobs. I discovered that I am a very quick learner and I have tended to do well at first but then struggle more as the job develops. There are some people who are able to do well in any situation. Well, unfortunately, that is not me. I have discovered how important it is for me to be working with the right people. In some circumstances, I have got on fine and had very few difficulties doing what was expected of me. In such cases, I am not disabled by having AS. In other circumstances, I have worked with people who I felt had very different communication styles to me (indirect, rather than direct). This can lead to some communication problems, where one person is communicating something and the other is misunderstanding, and in many cases, neither party even realising about the miscommunication. I have tried really hard to succeed in all my jobs, but in some circumstances, this did not seem to be good enough, and I did not understand why my rule "work hard = success" was not working. I have felt lost and in a scary atmosphere where things were out of my control and where other people were unpredictable.

One challenge I have found with jobs is that they tend to develop and change as the person's experience increases; for example, the employee may be given more responsibility as they become more senior. As a person not particularly fond of change, this is difficult because it is hard to feel secure in my ability to do the job. All I can know is whether I seem to be managing what is expected of me at the present moment. But in jobs which change, the fact of managing okay at one point in time cannot be used to predict future success.

Although I definitely can develop and improve, my rate of doing this may be slower and/or I may be starting from a lower starting point. Either of these things may mean that I am not able

31

to keep pace with my colleagues in some aspects of the job. For example, when I left University and first started work, I did not feel comfortable talking with clients on the phone. I believe that I was less skilled at doing this task than most people would have been, due to having less well developed social skills. Later on, I became fairly comfortable talking on the phone, but I still found meeting with clients in person very difficult. The demands of understanding and processing what clients are saying, working out what I have to say, in addition to being concerned with how I look and maintaining a professional image, can be a bit of a challenge for a person such as me who monoprocesses. For example, a client might be talking to me at the same time as drawing a picture. I would have to simultaneously:

(1) look at the drawing;
(2) listen to the client; and
(3) think to figure out what it all meant;

but I can only properly do one of these actions at once. However, most Neurotypical people can do all three at once, and therefore would not have this particular challenge. So, I believe that the speed at which I can become confident conducting meetings in a business setting will be slower than for most Neurotypical people.

Other challenges about work include that most tasks do not have exact answers to them. I like answers that have no doubt, like the answer 7.3 in a maths problem. For me, life is black and white, and I struggle to deal with grey areas. But, since we now have computers to do black and white thinking, many jobs involve an element of judgement and plenty of grey areas. Doing this kind of thinking can make me feel anxious, because I like to know that I am doing things "right". At worst, this can lead to panic attacks. One compensation for this is to have a colleague check my work, which makes a grey-type job into a black and white one for me. If they say my work is fine, I stop worrying about it. If they want something changed, I change it so it is now "correct".

Another challenge in work concerns seeing the big picture of a situation. I am good at being accurate and paying attention to detail, but it is harder to see the big picture. Indeed, I get the feeling that other people find it quite easy to see the overview of a situation. I can do this too, but I have to see the big picture through laboriously threading all the little details together, which takes a lot of effort.

Perhaps the biggest difficulty in employment is that most other people do not have these issues and it can easily be assumed that you are just like everyone else. Work expectations are set by the skills and abilities of the majority of people and I have found that I am advanced in some areas and behind in others, in ways that some of my employers have not expected. For most of my working life so far, I did not have a diagnosis of AS, and this can hinder understanding. It was only after obtaining this diagnosis that I even recognised and understood some of the difficulties that I was having and thus was able to start disclosing and dealing with them.

Turning now to another area of life, I have a very nice set of friends. Like my friends at university, they do laugh at me, but in a nice way. I used to say everything that was on my mind, but I am learning to be more discrete. Someone told me that anything you offer into the public arena is seen as fair-game for people to use against you or poke fun at, on the basis that they assume since you have offered it, you must be okay with whatever it is. For example, it distresses me when people accidentally become offended at something that I say. Since it bothers me, I used to talk about these incidents, hoping to feel better, but this only caused a lot of teasing, which I did not like at all. I do not find that me unintentionally upsetting other people is funny. I try to have a sense of humour about a lot of things, but not about this. So, now I have learned that if I am not comfortable with something, it is best not to discuss it in public.

Are you eating an orange?

Three years ago, one of my friends suggested I might be autistic and I had to take a decision. I could reject the idea as too unpalatable and try to forget it. Or, I could face the knowledge, probably be miserable for a bit, and then hopefully end up in a better place at the other side, which is the route I chose and is what indeed happened. If I was autistic and just denied it, I reasoned, I would still have all of the problems Autism can cause, but I would be less able to deal with them because of not having the required knowledge. So, denial did not seem to be a sensible choice.

The first thing I did was to read about Asperger Syndrome on Wikipedia. The diagnostic criteria were not very helpful - how on earth should I know if I have problems with social interaction sufficient for a diagnosis? However, Wikipedia included a very helpful page with seventeen easy to understand characteristics written in simple language. These characteristics are listed in the chapter "What are Autism and Asperger Syndrome?" I recognised almost all of these in myself. So, from that point on, I was quite sure that I was an aspie.

The next thing I did was to go to my doctor and ask for a diagnosis. My doctor was dissuasive, asking me if I was sure I really wanted a diagnosis because no help would be available even if the diagnosis was positive. I said that I was sure. She then asked what I wanted her to do, so I explained to her that the procedure was to refer me to the local Adult Autism Centre to get the diagnosis and I gave her the contact details. She then referred me. I was not impressed at my doctor's lack of knowledge. Not only did I have to identify myself as being on the spectrum, but I also needed to persuade my doctor to refer me for diagnosis and then tell her how to do it.

I then hit a long waiting list, which did not do my anxiety very much good. So, despite the usual advice against diagnosing yourself and reading up on any particular medical condition, this is what I did. I started at my local library and used inter-library lending to devour everything I could on the subject. I remember being disappointed by a book entitled "Solutions for Adults with AS" as after reading it, I did not feel that I had been given any solutions!

I certainly was miserable for a bit. I did not know how to react to this new label, which seemed to explain me so well but which turned my self-identity on its head and meant reading terms like "impairment", "disorder", "brain lesions", knowing they were applied to me. I started to wonder whether I had any free will at all, if all of the features of my personality which correspond so well with the autistic traits were inevitable, and whether I was just some robot, programmed to function with an "autistic operating system" instead of a "Neurotypical operating system". I calmed down when I thought about my friend, who already had a diagnosis of AS, and I realised that I was not the same as him. Therefore, I reasoned that autistic people are not identical and are in fact as diverse as the non-autistic population. So, good, I am not an autistically-programmed robot, that was something.

Around three months later, I got my appointment at the Autism Centre. I had decided to only go as far as the pre-diagnostic questionnaire, because I was concerned that "autistic" should not be on my medical records, in case that could be held against me in the future. An example I imagined was a judge deciding in the future that I, as a future hypothetical autistic mother, was not competent to care for my future, hypothetical, children. Not too likely, I know, but I did not want to take any chances. My concerns were listened to and it was suggested that I come to a pre-diagnostic session, which is not the same as a full diagnosis, but which takes about three hours, after which my diagnostician would have a very good idea as to whether I was on the spectrum or not and would be able to tell me with 99% certainty, without that counting as an actual diagnosis.

Before I went into my appointment, I asked myself why I was doing this. Either the diagnostician would say that I was an aspie, and I would agree or alternatively, she would say that I was not an aspie, and I would disagree and continue in my belief that I was on the spectrum. I rather arrogantly thought that I was skilful enough at pretending to be normal, that there was a chance I would slip through the net. I predicted that I would get a wishy-washy "maybe" answer, with a lot of talk about perhaps on the borderline and use of the words "possibly a very mild case". To my considerable surprise and shock, the diagnostician said she had absolutely no doubt that I was on the spectrum. The positive answer was not a surprise in itself; it was the complete lack of doubt and mention of any borderline status that I was not expecting. My ears temporarily switched off whilst I absorbed the impact of that, but afterwards, I did not feel much different because the real shock had been my friend's initial suggestion several months ago; the appointment was just confirmation of what I already knew.

A few years later, I am now over the shock of the change to my self-identity and I can read the word "impairment" without feeling pain. I have read many personal accounts written by autistic people and met many fantastic people in the Autism world at the National Autistic Society, the Autism Centre and at University, where I recently completed a Post-Graduate Certificate in Autism. Some of these people are on the spectrum, others are not, and all have contributed to my feeling more at home in this strange new world. Now, if I read, learn or hear something overly negative about Autism, I am more able to ignore it.

More recently, I returned to the Autism Centre and I now have a full, official confirmed diagnosis. I chose to go "official" because I realised that being able to declare myself as disabled was going to be important. To my surprise, according to ICD-10 my diagnosis is not Asperger Syndrome, but is Childhood Autism (Kanner's Autism), because of various developmental delays evidenced before the age of three (no crawling, no imaginative play, no babbling at all, and no talking before age two). However, I also have a second diagnosis of Asperger Syndrome according to the

Gillberg criteria. So, lucky me, two labels for the price of one! An unexpected side-effect of my official diagnosis is that it has enabled me to apply for Disability Living Allowance, which I had not previously been aware could be applicable to me.

Since I already knew with certainty that I was on the spectrum, my official diagnosis was not much of a shock. However, it did cause considerable confusion as to why I had been put into the Autism box according to ICD-10 (the most official criteria), rather than the Asperger box. Whichever way I look at it, this does not make any sense. I have read what Donna Williams has written about the differences between herself and her aspie husband (Williams, 1996). In every single one of these differences, I am like the aspie husband and unlike autie Donna. I know lots of aspies and some auties and I cannot see any difference between me and the aspies. I have been told I have a very aspie-presentation. I have never experienced self-other problems (losing your sense of self when paying attention to something external to your body and losing track of your surroundings when paying attention to your internal state). I do not ever remember a time when I did not realise that other people's knowledge was different to mine. My sensory issues are on the mild side compared to those I know who have Kanner's Autism. I am more of a thinker than a doer. I am, and have always been, very verbal. I pay more attention to outside stimuli than my internal body messages. For as far back as I can remember, I have always used the system of interpretation and not the system of sensing.

Basically, there seem to be lots of differences between me and auties. I therefore conclude that I am most probably an aspie who has accidentally been put in the wrong box, very probably because the diagnostic criteria are incomplete and cannot usefully be used to distinguish between Autism and Aspergers in adults when relying on parental memories of thirty years ago. If my parents had said I talked at one year and eleven months, would that have made me officially an aspie, whereas talking at two years and zero months means Autism? It seems the margin of error in these things is too large for any reliable diagnosis at this age in any case. Also, children are very different and personality plays a part. If I had decided to try talking earlier (a simple fact of me making a decision) that might have changed my diagnosis. The personality trait of me being a perfectionist might have made me talk late, rather than any issue relating to Kanner's Autism. When I trust myself, my own reading, learning and understanding and when I compare myself to aspies and auties I know, I always come to the conclusion that I must be an aspie. Therefore, for the purposes of this book, I am going to put my official diagnosis of Kanner's Autism to one side, trust my instincts and call myself an aspie.

Please do not think this is because I have a prejudice against being an autie. I do not mind that at all in principle; I do not think of myself in any way "better" than auties. Some of my friends are auties and I would be proud to share their diagnosis. If my diagnosis as an autie fitted well with the evidence I have, then I would be happy to embrace it as who I am. I am just looking for the place on the spectrum that I seem to properly fit, and my only problem with the Kanner's Autism diagnosis is that it does not seem to fit me at all. You can make up your own mind after reading this book.

I am now fairly secure in myself in my aspie status. It means I can stop blaming myself so much when personal interactions go wrong, which they sometimes do. In fact, there have been several instances where I have realised that the fault lay partly with the other side, their prejudices and stereotypes, which are getting in the way of their understanding me. It has increased my self-awareness. It means having a realistic, objective view of my weaknesses, so that I can hopefully make better life choices. For example, I now know that if I tried to become a teacher, that would be pretty disastrous (think monoprocessing and thirty children), whereas before, I might have contemplated it as a career choice. And I now know I am not alone. There are many people like me in the world; I just have to open my eyes and find them. I think the world would be a poorer place without Autism, because it would be lacking a lot of bright, ethical, colourful, wonderful people and even a good number of its geniuses, for example Beethoven, Newton and Einstein.

Apparently, being diagnosed has changed me as a person. I suppose this is not really surprising, as many big life events can change you, such as leaving home for the first time, the death of a parent or an episode of depression. The change is gradual (like improving at a foreign language) and so not particularly obvious when it is happening. However, other people have noticed a difference. I guess this is just a little warning that if you take on something this important, it does change you, and probably in a way which you cannot (even if you wished to) reverse. It is said that autistic folk do not, in general, like change. However, this is also true for some NTs. Changing yourself could change your relationships with other people around you. I find it really hard to be aware of how I might have changed, but perhaps I am now more independent, less needy and also busier, because learning about Autism has opened all sorts of new doors for me. One of my friends was quite concerned about the change in me, and she said she prefers the "old me" to the "new one". I do not actually feel like I have become a different person, although my focus and perspective have changed and the path has certainly not been easy. However, if there has been a change, I am quite happy with the "new me". So, this is just a warning that learning about Autism might cause a change in you and it is possible that not everyone will like it.

It is also possible that someone else in your life will have more difficulty adjusting to your Autism diagnosis than you do. I (and I think many other autistic people) tend to approach things in a very logical way, and that was certainly how I approached my diagnosis. It was simply more logical to accept it and learn about it than not. However, someone reacting on an emotional basis rather than a logical basis might have a harder time. This is not me telling you not to go for it. On the contrary, just letting you know about some friction you could face on the way. Forewarned is forearmed…

Life is now okay. It is not exactly how I pictured, but in the general scheme of things, things are settling down. I currently work part-time in a low-stress job which is going very well, which has made me financially pretty poor but has given me a decent amount of free time in the week to pursue my own interests and goals. I am still immature; my parents are still waiting for me to grow up. I like helium balloons, somersaults and Harry Potter. I like spending time with children - preferably the under-elevens. Under-elevens are mostly literal and are not yet into the crazy teenage world that I did not get at the time and I still do not get now. And somehow, without explanation, children recognise that I am just like them. I have a flat to live in and no debts. I am not married but I am happy being single and I am happy living on my own. I want to have children in the future. I often still find myself battling to be understood, but I now know enough people who do understand me and who allow me to be myself, that life is pretty good. At the moment, a lot of my free time is taken up with Autism - learning about Autism, volunteering, and increasingly my socialising is with others on the spectrum. This may look a bit overbalanced to others, but it feels okay to me.

Why Diagnose?

Sometimes people are surprised that I was not identified and diagnosed as autistic as a child. I certainly had many features which match the diagnostic criteria for AS and Autism, and which could have been recognised. For example, I was extremely poor at sports, particularly ball-skills. I had awful posture, could not understand facial expressions and was not aware of my own facial expressions. Making friends was difficult and I got on better with younger children. I did not know how to comfort people who were sad and I tended to act the same way regardless of social context. I had an unusually intense interest in trampolining. Most of these are still true today. The spectrum is not something you grow out of.

Tony Attwood estimates that even today, only 50% of aspies are recognised and diagnosed (Attwood, 2006). I suppose this might well apply to high functioning Autism too. Attwood also noted that girls with AS ("the invisible end of the spectrum") are more difficult to recognise and diagnose due to coping and camouflaging mechanisms, such as being good at acting. Attwood also mentioned the tactic of being well-behaved and polite, to avoid active participation in class, and this was certainly one that I used.

I did not have meltdowns in class, came top in every test, and was generally more ignored than bullied, so why would anyone in school notice? I was not particularly unusual compared to my family, so why would my family notice? I was relatively healthy, so why would a doctor notice? Hence, being a girl, with relatively minor sensory processing difficulties, with parents who put a lot of effort into my development, and with enough intelligence, rote memory and diligence to work around the difficulties, I left school with only one friend but at the top of my year and with no-one suspecting I was on the spectrum.

I am not convinced that a diagnosis of Autism is always a good thing. I certainly started off very much doubting it because of the huge shock it can bring to your self-identity and because of the very depressing way that Autism is often described. It really is very difficult to believe your whole life that you are normal and to suddenly, one day, realise that you are not normal, you have a "disorder" and that you will never be normal.

So, should you tell a very high functioning person, who is doing pretty well in their life and who does not have any major problems, that they are impaired in the social, communication and imaginative realms? Is it not kinder to leave them in ignorance? Particularly when there is not presently very much help out there for adults, beyond what you can do for yourself. Following my informal diagnosis, there was no post-diagnostic course or anything like that. I had a limited number of post-diagnostic appointments at the Autism Centre (but most of these happened years after my initial diagnosis due to the centre only being open in working hours). To my surprise, there was no social skills course available or anything to help me compensate for my areas of weakness. So, my experience has been to have to take the diagnosis and get on with it myself.

However, the more I learn, the more I am becoming more pro-diagnosis. The main reason for this is that, contrary to the view of most of the Autism field, Autism is not confined to the mental sphere. Fundamentally, I believe it is not just a matter of checking if someone has anxiety or depression, OCD, worries too much or is unemployed, and if not, they are fine and do not need any support or to be bothered by finding out they are on the spectrum. Autism permeates far more than just the mind. It means having a different kind of body, a different kind of mind and a different kind of soul, and ignorance of this does not do people any good. If you are ignorant about your different kind of body, you cannot learn how to make your body work better and medical treatment you receive might be inappropriate. If you are ignorant about your different kind of soul, you might make inappropriate life choices and never understand where you are going wrong.

In my opinion, it is not enough to say: "I do not have any difficulties in the mental sphere, therefore it is irrelevant to me if I am on the spectrum or not". Even if you do not need this label to get understanding from people, no matter how skilled the aspie, I think there is always something to be gained from a higher level of self-awareness, which I find is what knowing about Autism has brought me. And even if you are pretty sorted in your own life, what about your family, who may also need help and understanding (quite apart from the hereditary risk of any children you may have being on the spectrum too)?

I know one woman who might be diagnosable. Two other people have told me that she is autistic and from having met her a few times, her social interaction is so unusual, I have to agree. However, speaking with her, I find out that she is apparently unaware that she is on the spectrum. She is having bowel troubles and I feel pretty sure that if she was on the Gluten-Free, Casein-Free (GF-CF) Diet, this would help her a lot. However, I am not sure that she would be capable of implementing the diet herself without considerable assistance, which she is not receiving. I was stunned that she was not even aware that she is on the spectrum, despite it being apparent to other people. Not a great place to start. I also learned from this that it is not always possible for me to help someone, even if I think I know a possible solution.

So - to diagnose or not to diagnose? On the whole, I think it is usually beneficial - diagnosis has helped me personally in many ways, and even if it does not help others so much, there is probably something to be gained for most people. My main reservation would be if the person is already so psychologically scarred that they would be unable to accept and come to terms with the diagnosis. After all, aspies and auties, particularly non-diagnosed adults, are likely to have a great many war wounds to their self-esteem.

An example of how much damage the current public attitude to Autism is doing comes from the reaction I got from three people after I disclosed my diagnosis of AS to them. These people all responded by telling me that they already knew or suspected as much. I was really surprised that none of them had informed me! One of these people was someone who often used an indirect communication style with me. I was particularly surprised that person had guessed, because indirect communication is an especially difficult style for most people on the spectrum to understand.

So, why did none of these people tell me they thought I was on the spectrum? I believe that they (and possibly other people too) were not telling me because the public perception of being autistic is pretty negative. For people to tell me they think I am autistic risks hurting my feelings and might be taken as an insult. I appreciate the intention here, but I did not get help or a diagnosis, because other people were sitting around recognising I was autistic, but being far too polite and tactful to inform me! I think that this public perception of Autism and this kind of consequence is unacceptable.

I have made a few scary, carefully considered experiments in saying to other people that I think they might be on the spectrum too, with the aim of being helpful. No-one who I have said this to has actually wanted to hear it. However, no-one has punched me on the nose or fallen out with me either. All responses have been on the lines of: "thanks for your thoughts but I do not think that is relevant". These logical rather than emotional responses were fortunate for me, because I do not enjoy being punched on the nose. Receiving these logical responses makes me think that I may be correct about them being on the spectrum, because us spectrum folk tend to react in a logical way, rather than in an emotional way. Equally, however, they might just be very nice, calm, NT people, who appreciated the intent behind what I said and therefore decided not to take offense.

It seems likely to me that some people would not want to acknowledge they are on the spectrum because they know that their self-image could not bear to recognise such a diagnosis. And who am I to say that is the wrong approach? They know themselves better than I do. I am not sure that many NTs, even in the Autism world, realise how devastating the initial shock of a diagnosis of Autism can be.

What I am finding, to my surprise, is that the highest functioning people, who have the brains and the ability to learn about Autism and improve their lives in significant ways (for example, by sorting out their sensory problems thus lowering overload and anxiety), are actually the most resistant to doing so due to being in denial, and are therefore the least likely to get any help they may need. This is very ironic. To stop this disturbing trend, what needs to change is the public's attitude to Autism, so that it is no longer steeped in negativity. Then, people may not be so horrified by the idea that they could be on the spectrum that they cannot accept it and instead throw up a huge wall of denial.

So, from the fact that most people were not telling me that I was on the spectrum, I realise that society's attitude is that you should not tell someone if you suspect they are on the spectrum. From the lack of positive uptake of everyone to whom I disclosed my theories about *them* being on the spectrum, I can see that society's view may be the right thing in many cases. However, I *did* want to know, and I cannot discount the possibility that someone else I know might too.

I believe the present statistics are that only around 15% of people diagnosed as being on the spectrum are in full-time employment. However, I believe that I am far from unusual in being both on the spectrum and employed, for the simple reason that it is obvious to me that there are lots of undiagnosed aspies out there in the workplace. However, if society's attitude that "Autism = Bad" continues, the high functioning, employed people will continue to reject diagnosis and the stereotype of most autistic people being low functioning will continue. This in turn makes it harder for the difficulties of autistic people in mainstream society to be recognised and understood. In the absence of recognition, it is possible to make all sorts of wrong assumptions about the behaviour of someone on the spectrum and the idea that Autism could be a factor may never be considered.

Are you eating an orange?

Sensory Processing

In this chapter, I am going to talk about sensory and perceptual differences in Autism.

When talking about Autism, the professionals generally like to start with what they can observe: the Triad of Impairments. I think this is the wrong place to start, because the Triad is the effect and not the cause. If, unusually, the professionals do not start from the Triad, they start with the more obvious sensory differences: hypersensitivities and hyposensitivities. Whilst this is slightly better, I am still not satisfied; what causes the sensory sensitivities? That does not seem to be the best starting point either.

Gestalt Perception and Monoprocessing

Since I like to begin at the beginning, I will start with gestalt perception, which is the closest thing I have found to the root of Autism...

Gestalt Perception

One theory is that autistic people have a gestalt perception style. Gestalt perception is the inability to distinguish between foreground and background information. According to Donna Williams (an autie), this is like having "a brain with no sieve" (Bogdashina, 2003, p 46). You can have gestalt perception in all sensory modalities.

Gestalt perception leads to information overload (being flooded with detail), because not everything can be broken up into meaningful bits. It is impossible (even for NTs) to process every detail of a situation. However, whereas NTs, with their more reliable filtering system, will process important parts, we spectrum folk process parts which just happen to get our attention (Bogdashina, 2003).

Auditory Gestalt Perception

I experience auditory gestalt perception when I cannot follow what someone is saying because other people are also talking near-by. For example, once, in a crowded street, I was unable to hear anything on my mobile phone, whilst my German friend (who should theoretically have found this harder than me because she was not using her mother-tongue) managed just fine. I also cannot hear a telephone conversation if someone else is talking in the same room. I also remember an instance recently, in a noisy pub with loud music. I was in a conversation with three other people, and I could not make sense of what any of them were saying. I could not contribute to the conversation, not because I was too shy, but because I could not hear enough words to understand the meaning of their sentences. In contrast, the other three people were communicating just fine. I cannot describe how completely frustrating this is, and it leaves me completely exhausted through trying so hard to understand what is going on. I went home feeling a bit sad, a bit alien, very autistic, and with a big sense of "this is not fair!"

Not being able to hear what people are saying is widely reported by other aspies and auties in their personal accounts. For example, Luke Jackson has difficulty in distinguishing between background and foreground noises (Jackson, 2002b). Neil Shepherd explains that he has difficulty tracking more than one conversation at a time and that it descends into generic noise rather than distinctive conversation (Edmonds & Beardon, 2008). Liane Holliday Willey finds that "sounds seemed to glue themselves to one another so that it was gruelling to pick them apart" (Holliday Willey, 1999, p. 88).

Jansson-Verkasalo et al. (2003) recorded event-related potentials (ERPs) for syllables and tones in a group of aspie children and a control group. Their results indicate that aspies have problems in auditory discrimination and that their auditory sensory processing is deficient. Also, in my personal opinion, another factor which may disrupt proper hearing/comprehension is by eating foods to which autistic bodies are intolerant, such as gluten.

Visual Gestalt Perception

Visual gestalt perception means that my sight is more "fractured" than other people's sight. There is nothing wrong with my eyes, but my brain processes visual information differently than normal. I experienced visual gestalt perception when I walked into an unfamiliar room (my tutor's office) and felt overcome by visual information. So I started by examining a bookshelf, and afterwards, turned to examine the rest of the room, piece-meal. Another example was with a friend, in the executive lounge of Amsterdam airport. They had a very funky seating arrangement, with five chairs positioned around a table and a massive "desk lamp" which was about nine feet tall standing between two of the chairs, with its arm stretched towards the centre of the seating arrangement and a big light upon the arm. I had been in this lounge, at this seating arrangement, for about fifteen minutes. My friend then went away to get a coffee. In this quiet time, I noticed this massive lighting arrangement for the first time. I was really amused that I had managed to completely miss this monumental lamp, which I had been sitting right next to, for the previous fifteen minutes. To me, it was simply one of many random details of the room which I had just happened not to process. To an NT, I am sure an object of such great size and proximity would have been caught by their "brain sieve" as an important object to notice straight away.

It is difficult to imagine how other people see me, but I think that my visual gestalt perception has the effect of making me look generally a bit surprised, and maybe a bit curious (like a baby animal, before it has got bored with life - you know, the difference between lambs and sheep?). It also means that it takes me typically longer than other people to make sense of new surroundings, like when I walk into a new room. Of course, I work quite hard to process the surroundings, and my gestalt perception is probably not be as extreme as some other autistic people, so my delay is of the order of a few seconds whilst I try to make sense of a new situation. I have recognised the same slightly surprised look in some photographs of other autistic people. One of my friends was told at work that they should stop looking surprised. This really annoys me, because they cannot help it.

Effects of Gestalt Perception

Gestalt perception has an effect on confidence, because I have a sense of bewilderment in a new situation, which makes me feel "on the back foot". It has the biggest effect when moving into a new location. This is because staying in one place for any amount of time gives me the opportunity to "add up" all the remaining details and become less confused. Also, if the room is familiar to me, I do not need to process so much, because my memory fills in the gaps which are not processed. I do not have to work out where my kettle is every time I go into my kitchen, because I know where I keep it. But unfamiliar rooms take a bit longer. However, new situations often correspond with the start of a communicative interaction, so at the same time as being overwhelmed with all these new details, I am expected to perform and interact at high speed with a person. This is not easy.

One day at University, when we arrived for one of our lectures, the tables and chairs in the lecture room were in a different configuration than usual. This did not bother me at all. However, to my astonishment, another student completely freaked out. This student could not enter the room for quite a long while. I was so surprised that a different arrangement of furniture could cause such a big problem that I am afraid my reaction was all astonishment, whereas it should have been understanding and sympathetic. Next time, I will be prepared. I think that their reaction was due to total confusion and overload by the familiar structure they rely upon to manage within the classroom being taken away; perhaps there was also an element of shock, because they were expecting a familiar environment.

Monoprocessing

Bogdashina (2003) describes various compensatory strategies used (sometimes unconsciously) by spectrum folk, to survive information overload. One of these is monoprocessing. Monoprocessing (or monotropism) means only being able to process information from one sensory system at a time. This contrasts with NTs' polytropism, which allows processing from several sensory systems simultaneously. Monotropic attention can be compared to a narrow torch beam/attention tunnel, whilst polytropic attention is more broadly diffused (a wider beam).

In my opinion, monoprocessing is the single most important thing to know about Autism, because it can account for almost everything else, and yet it is frequently ignored completely in the literature/Autism training sessions. Monoprocessing is a good compensatory strategy for overload, because it helps to keep the one channel that is "on" functioning most efficiently (Bogdashina, 2003).

There are seven sensory systems: seeing, hearing, tactile, smell, taste, propriosensory, and vestibular (Dunn, Saiter & Rinner, 2002). With monoprocessing, each of these seven sensory systems has its separate channel. Personally, I would add an eighth "thinking" channel to these seven.

I experience monoprocessing all the time. If I spend a long time in one session writing this book, "thinking" is on and the rest of the channels are off. I might get very cold and hungry, but may not notice until I have finished the session. When I walk to work, usually "thinking" is on, with the occasionally "seeing". In both cases, I do not hear background noises. When I do try to listen, the traffic seems so loud that I am glad that my ears quickly switch off. If "thinking" is on, this precludes all sensory input and I take in nothing on a conscious level. Hence, after a long while of always walking/cycling the same route to work, I did not know what shops I passed. In cafes, I cannot hear the background music unless I specifically focus on it (which I cannot do at the same time as having a conversation), so I do not know any words of pop songs. In my local park, I sometimes try to listen to the birds singing, but my ears switch off almost immediately. I do not taste my dinner if I am watching TV. During an exam, my friend was really bothered by the sound of drilling outside the exam hall. My response was "what drilling?". I was completely unaware of the drilling because "thinking" was on and "hearing" was off.

Other spectrum folk also share this experience. Wendy Lawson describes her "tunnel vision" (Lawson, 2001, p. 33) and how listening and then being required to make a decision, without due processing time, causes channel switching difficulties.

Donna Williams has a more extreme form of monoprocessing than me (her attention tunnel is narrower), and cannot simultaneously experience herself, plus anything else (Williams, 1998). This is called a "self-other problem" and seems to be experienced by more auties than aspies. This means processing either self (internal messages such as thoughts, feelings, hunger, cold) or other (incoming sensory information such as sights, sounds, touch), but not both simultaneously. The state of "all self, no other" means you know who you are and what you think but you are oblivious to the world. In this state, you will probably appear aloof. The state of "all other, no self" means you are processing sensory information from your surroundings but you cannot access your thoughts and feelings so you have to act on automatic pilot. In this state, you will probably appear passive. People who have this self-other problem might experience "loss of self" under sensory overload conditions, which causes their state to switch into "all other, no self".

Are you eating an orange?

One of my main responses to being overwhelmed by detail is to switch into the thinking channel. It is more pleasant because, unlike using the other channels, I only think one thought at a time, and being in the thinking channel blocks all of those un-processable sights and sounds completely.

Some effects of Monoprocessing on Communication and Social Interaction

In real life, with high task processing demands, social cues can be missed if they fall outside the attention tunnel. Hence, social situations can be misunderstood. The cognitive effects of monoprocessing also inhibit simultaneous awareness of the viewpoints of others (Murray, Lesser & Lawson, 2005). People who monoprocess can either focus on an object/experience, or on another person, but not on both (failure in joint attention). This leads to fewer shared experiences and to failure to understand the meaning of interactions, which hinders social development and causes Theory of Mind problems (Bogdashina, 2003).

Monoprocessing causes delays when important information comes in from several channels simultaneously (which happens in every interaction with another person). This is because we have to process in series, whereas NTs can process in parallel.

Monoprocessing also affects communication. Communication includes a number of components:

a)   speech;
b)   facial expressions;
c)   body language; and
d)   lip movements.

(Iarocci & McDonald, 2006).

When someone talks to me, my hearing channel is on, so I hear the words but do not receive the visual components (b), (c) or (d).

52

Consequently, I get the literal meaning. However, if a non-literal meaning is meant (conveyed by facial expression/body language), I might miss this. Being aware of this, I once did an experiment to see if I could read the body language of my conversation partner. I had to stop my experiment after about six seconds because my ears had switched off and it would have been rude not to listen.

Since I do not have any visual/contextual clues, it is hard to guess any misheard words. This is supported by the findings of Alcántara, Weisblatt, Moore & Bolton (2004), who found the required ratio of speech-to-noise to correctly identify speech was higher for people on the spectrum than for controls and that the controls were better able to use temporal and spectral dips in the background noise to deduce any misheard words.

Monoprocessing also makes me less aware of the overall context, because my attention tunnel is too narrow. So, if a piece of information does not match the context (which would ordinarily cue recognition of a non-literal interpretation), I might miss this. Consequently, my perception is literal, and without automatic interpretation, which instead requires conscious effort. Blackburn's experiences also support this: "Most things I take at face value, without judging or interpreting them... I do not normally integrate things or see them as connected unless I actively look for a connection." (Blackburn, 1999, as cited in Bogdashina, 2003, p. 45.)

For example, I was with a group of friends and the conversation turned to people's habits of drinking alcohol. One friend said that they spent half their salary on beer. I immediately starting thinking in my head about what their salary probably was and dividing that in two. I felt stunned that anyone could spend so much money on alcohol - what a waste - and my eyebrows flew upwards in shock. A few seconds later, the thought that my friend was probably exaggerating entered my head. But I was too late; my eyebrows had already betrayed my original thoughts and my friend had noticed. He said (sarcastically): "Yes Debi, I spend

Are you eating an orange?

literally half my salary on beer" and everyone laughed at me, but in a nice way.

The statement about how much money my friend spent on alcohol per year was completely outrageous, because no-one would spend tens of thousands of pounds per year on beer. However, despite the statement being so obviously wrong, I still processed the statement literally first, before starting to question it. Hence, I believe this is a good example of my literal perception, without automatic interpretation. No-one else in my group of friends reacted with any kind of shock to my friend's statement, which leads me to think that they interpreted the statement in full context automatically (and very speedily), without the cognitive steps that I had to take.

The Seven Sensory Systems

OK, so we have looked at the different processing styles of gestalt perception and monoprocessing. But it is not only how we *process* sensory information that is different; also there can be large differences in how we *perceive* the sensory information in the first place.

Although not even included in the diagnostic criteria (ICD-10, 1994), many studies point to a high prevalence of unusual sensory processing in spectrum folk, and some consider Autism to be primarily a sensory perceptual deficit, for example, Van Dalen, cited in Bogdashina (2003). A literature review found estimates of people on the spectrum experiencing unusual sensory processing to be from 30%-100% (Dawson & Watling, 2000). Watling (2001), cited in Iarocci et al. (2006), found significant differences on eight out of ten sensory factors. Sensory differences are a good predictor of Autism in the first two years of life, are lifelong, and occur in the absence of hearing/visual defects (Iarocci et al., 2006). Some unusual sensory features include hyper- and hyposensitivities to stimulation and fluctuations between these two states (Harrison & Hare, 2004).

So, what are the seven sensory systems? Well, there are the five senses that we learn about in school - sight, hearing, smell, taste and touch. Then, there are two additional sensory systems that we are not generally taught about in school; propriosensory and vestibular. The propriosensory system is how you know where different parts of your body are in relation to each other. For example, as I am typing this, I have an awareness of where my left foot is, although I cannot see it (it is beneath the desk), I cannot hear it (I am not tapping it) and I cannot smell it, taste it or touch it. The vestibular system is how you know where your body is relative to the world. For example, if I were on a roller coaster with my eyes shut tight, I would still know when I was upside down, thanks to my vestibular sensory system.

Are you eating an orange?

In my case, I have relatively minor sensory differences, as follows:

Sight - hypersensitive. In group photos in sunlight, my eyes are watering whilst everyone else is fine. I also have some difficulties with perceiving things at their correct distance. This means going downstairs can be hard, because I cannot judge precisely where the next step is. I also have quite a noticeable Pulfrich effect - when objects pass close to my face but are not going to hit me, I flinch involuntarily, even when it is explained that the object will not, in fact, hit my face. Most Neurotypical people, undergoing the same test, do not flinch.

Hearing - hypersensitive. At an underground train station, I noticed that I flinched when a train went past but other people did not. However, my sensitivity was apparently mild compared to another aspie in our group, who flung her hands up to cover her ears very dramatically.

Smell - usually hyposensitive but occasionally hypersensitive. I cannot usually smell things unless they are directly under my nose. One day, whilst at work, I was (completely unconsciously) sniffing the skin underneath my watch, which was slightly sweaty. A colleague asked me, with some surprise, what I was doing. I was startled and actually had no idea because I was not doing it consciously. However, I realised that I did not want to stop, despite having my weirdness pointed out to me in public. It seemed somehow to be helping me to keep calm and focussed on the difficult piece of work I was doing. I now realise that I was seeking out extra smell sensory input to balance my hyposensitivity to smell. Hence, on the whole, I am hyposensitive. However, in a perfume store or soap shop, I cannot stand the strong smells and feel like I must escape immediately, revealing quite a significant hypersensitivity as well.

Taste - probably hyposensitive, or normal. I am not a particularly fussy eater when it comes to taste and I do not mind about different textures of food. However, I am sometimes hypersensitive to strong tastes, such as goats' milk and fish.

Touch - hyposensitive. Wearing a tight-hugging elasticated head band and sleeping under lots of bed covers provides additional tactile input and makes me calmer.

Propriosensory - hypersensitive and hyposensitive. Hypersensitive, on the part of my body to which I am paying attention. Hyposensitive, if I am not thinking about my body at all, or for the parts of my body I am not thinking about.

Vestibular - hyposensitive. I love trampolining, balancing on fences, swimming, diving, hand-stands, forward rolls, gymnastics, Heelys™, ice skating and roller coasters.

The extent of people's sensory differences can vary hugely. My differences are apparent because I have thought about these and worked them out, but previously I was unaware than my sensory perception was at all unusual. In the grand scheme of things, I am only probably two out of ten for sensory dysfunction, which is on the mild side of things compared to some other people on the spectrum. However, it is very common for people with even massive sensory differences to be unaware that their sensory perception is unusual. Since you can never step out of your own head and into someone else's, *no-one* (autistic or NT) knows how other people are experiencing the world and it is only natural to assume that you are getting the same sensory experience as everyone else.

Incidentally, I believe that being hyposensitive (under-sensitive) is often more fun than being hypersensitive. To regulate hyposensitivity, you just need to get yourself more of what you crave. For example, use brighter lights, put music on louder, give hard hugs, do more cartwheels. Whereas hypersensitivity can be harder to deal with because the environment can be intolerable, and to deaden the environment you might need dark glasses, ear plugs, a large personal space bubble and motion sickness tablets, to name but a few examples.

It is beyond the scope of this work to explain in any great detail about the sensory systems and I have only described some of the effects of hyper/hyposensitivities as they relate to me. How other people on the spectrum react to the same stimuli can be very different. For example, whilst I squint in bright sunlight (hypersensitive to visual input), a person who is hyposensitive to visual input might want to spend time staring at really bright lights. Also, whilst I love roller coasters (hyposensitive to vestibular input), someone who is hypersensitive to vestibular motion might feel like they are falling when they are only slightly tilted from vertical and might have a terrible fear of heights. The important thing to note here is that what you observe might vary wildly between two different people who could be hypersensitive and hyposensitive on different sensory channels to each other. Both may be on the spectrum, so one size definitely does not fit all for sensory solutions. For a brilliant explanation of this fascinating subject, I recommend Olga Bogdashina's "*Sensory Perceptual Issues in Autism and Asperger Syndrome*" (Bogdashina, 2003).

Furthermore, difficulties with sensory issues are not limited to hyper/hyposensitivities. For example, an imperfect co-ordination of two or more of these seven systems can cause its own problems, even if all systems are working perfectly well by themselves. For example, many people on the spectrum (and some people not on the spectrum) have dyspraxia, which may be defined as:

Dyspraxia = Mis-coordination of vision, propriosensory and vestibular input.

For example, someone with dyspraxia might struggle to catch a ball. In order to catch the ball, you need good visual input (to know the position of the ball), good vestibular input (to know where your head, body and hand are relative to the ground and your surroundings) and good propriosensory input (to know the position of your hand relative to your body and head, so that you can take account of your head not being in the same position as your hand and adjust for the fact that you are observing the ball coming towards your hand from a particular angle). Furthermore, you do not *only* need reliable data from these three sensory channels (which is already a problem for some autistic people); the vision, propriosensory and vestibular information has to be processed *simultaneously* to get the co-ordination correct. When trying to catch the ball, it will not work just to look but not to use the other two senses until the ball has already passed you by.

A person who is monoprocessing (which perhaps everyone on the spectrum is), has by definition a difficulty with experiencing two or more sensory systems simultaneously. Hence, I believe that people who monoprocess automatically meet this definition of dyspraxia.

My usage of the Sensory Channels

I would normally be unaware of smells, tastes, tactile, postural and vestibular information, as there is usually too much else going on to have the luxury of being able to pay attention to these. These channels are also the ones I am hyposensitive to (in contrast to being hypersensitive to seeing and hearing). I do not believe this is a coincidence. It could be that my visual and hearing channels, which I use the most, have become more developed and more sensitive *because* I use them the most. Hence, it could be that hyper- and hyposensitivities are also a consequence of monoprocessing.

My channels are fairly stably set on "thinking" and "seeing", with the odd "hearing" coming in, usually prompted by human speech, but not so much by background sounds. Compared to the experiences of some people on the spectrum, I am gradually concluding that I am relative lucky that my brain has organised itself so that it spends most time on the channels which are most helpful to interpret the world (thinking, seeing, hearing) and that these channels provide me with information that is (relatively) unscrambled. These might be the core features which allow me to be "high functioning". My biggest problem is *not* that any information I am getting is too flawed to be understood. My biggest problem is that I can only have one channel's worth of information at any one time.

This is not to say that I do not have any attentional problems - quite frequently, I cannot stay on the hearing channel as long as I need to. I used to annoy one of my bosses terribly (before we realised what was happening and we both found it funny), by frequently interrupting him without meaning to. What would happen was this. He would be explaining something to me. I would get confused about a particular detail. My thinking channel would immediately switch on, and my ears would switch off. I would carry on in my own world, trying to work out what he had meant. I would then be oblivious to the fact he was still talking. I would reach a conclusion about what he might have meant, or a question that I needed to ask. I would then ask my question/ check my conclusion, but unfortunately, he would still be talking. He would then look annoyed and tell me that I had interrupted. I would then apologise and we would carry on from there. After my boss realised that I did not mean to interrupt, his reaction changed. After that, whenever I interrupted him, he would start laughing. I would see that he was laughing and ask him what was so funny. He would then tell me I had interrupted him. Remembering my complete surprise that he would suddenly be laughing at me (and the fact that I had to ask him why he was laughing and could not guess), makes me really sure that my ears were completely switched off and I had no idea he was still speaking at the time. He jokes to me sometimes that I am not spending all my time on this planet. I think those are the times when I am using the thinking channel.

Sensory Prioritisation

I have a theory that most people on the spectrum use monoprocessing, but the effects can be different depending on what channel(s) the brain gives priority to. This will be highly specific to the individual.

To use myself as an example, here is what I think is my brain's list of priorities, (1) being the channel that attracts most of my attention and (8) attracting the least. This list is true for me when I am not talking and when no understandable English-language input is within earshot.

1. Thinking
2. Seeing
3. Hearing
4. Vestibular
5. Touch
6. Propriosensory
7. Taste
8. Smell

You can see from this list that generally, in my case, "thinking" and "seeing" are given the highest priority. "Hearing" comes third (definitely after "seeing") - my ears are switched off most of the time and background sounds tend not to register. Therefore, I find there is no point listening to music for relaxation because involuntarily, "thinking" will be on and "hearing" will be off. The longest I can concentrate on listening to music before my ears switch off is about twenty seconds. It also becomes obvious just how switched off my ears usually are when I spend time with my friend's daughter, who is two years old. She is very curious and is learning a lot of new words, so she often points and asks "what's that?". I usually understand when she is referring to something visual. However, sometimes she means a sound; once it was a dog barking. I did not know what she meant, because I was not on the hearing channel and therefore was not processing any background sounds at the time. When her Mum replied that it was a dog, I then heard the dog. Such things happen often.

However, there is one exception to this order of priorities; human speech immediately switches my channel to hearing. If there is some talking in English, in ear-shot, listening shoots to the top of the list, so that my brain's list of priorities changes to:

1. Hearing
2. Thinking
3. Seeing
4. Vestibular
5. Touch
6. Propriosensory
7. Taste
8. Smell

Hence, when someone is talking near me, my channel is involuntarily switched from thinking to hearing, and I cannot do anything that requires concentration and is not automatic.

It is quite hard to judge the exact order of the channels 4 to 8, because I use these channels so rarely, so this is my best guess. I do know that smell is definitely last though.

I have not been able to find any research in the area of sensory prioritisation, so I will have to give you my own theories on this point. Unlike me, some people use "hearing" more than "seeing". For example, my friend was unable to listen to a lecture because of a tiny sound of a mobile phone interfering with the computer equipment, which happened about every five minutes, but which I was pretty much unaware of (I think I only noticed it once or twice in the whole lecture). However, in the same lecture, I did notice the words which were being beamed through the overhead projector falling on the body of the lecturer when she inadvertently stepped in front of the projector. It looked funny to see written words across someone's body and it was (to me and most of my classmates) extremely obvious. In contrast, my auditory-dominant friend's eyes were switched off and she did not see that. So, in that lecture, I picked up visual information (and, fortunately for me, pretty much most of the speech of the lecture), whilst almost completely missing the background sound of the interference of the mobile (along with all touch, smell, vestibular and propriosensory, inputs). Whereas my friend was so on egg-shells at anticipating the next beeping jolt (which was probably painful to her ears), that she could neither use her eyes or actually listen to the lecture. I wish I had known that at the time, because I would have asked for the mobile phone to be switched off or moved to a place where it would not have caused the interference.

On another occasion, my friend nearly got run over because she was distracted by a sound, and therefore could not see an approaching car. She was crossing a road. A police siren sounded. Sound engulfed her universe and her vision immediately and completely switched off so she could not see anything. Her propriosensory sense is so unreliable, that if she cannot see, she cannot walk, because she does not know where her body is. So, even though she was in the middle of the road, she had to stop walking and wait for her sight to come back. In the meantime, the police car making the noise nearly ran her over. Pretty ironic really, as police sirens are supposed to make people more aware and able to get out of the way. Minshew, Sung, Jones, & Furman (2004) found ASD children to have more difficulty in maintaining their balance when their vision was occluded, and my friend seems to be an extreme example of this.

I only have one vaguely similar (traffic-related) experience, which was when I was driving and started to turn right, into the path of an oncoming car. However, that was not because of an interrupting sound. That was because I was talking (and therefore thinking) at the same time (thinking, for me, being dominant over seeing).

Are you eating an orange?

A "thought" got in my eyes. Luckily, the other person in the car yelled at me to stop.

For me, what channel is "on" is largely involuntary, but I am interested to find out whether I can develop this into more of a conscious choice. I am sure this should be possible, at least to some extent. I am glad that my brain has opted for the lists of priorities given above, because it is quite a sensible list for making sense of the world. My brain ensures that I do not ignore what people say, by giving me no other option but listening when someone is talking. This is a good survival tactic and contributes greatly to me being "high functioning". My brain also prioritises seeing and listening over smelling and tasting, which is also useful for picking up most important information. It seems likely that brains experiment during development and that most people's brains would choose the optimum set-up for them. For example, my visual and auditory processing difficulties are not severe, so using vision and hearing is sensible for me. However, someone with severe sensory processing problems on the visual or auditory channels might find information from these channels meaningless, so their brain might choose the following list of priorities:

1. Touch
2. Taste
3. Vestibular
4. Smell
5. Thinking
6. Propriosensory
7. Seeing
8. Hearing

Does this sound like anyone you know? Of course, having such a list of priorities would make understanding what is going on much harder for that person, but given their severe sensory issues, this might be their optimum way of being (in the absence of any interventions to improve their sensory processing). Perhaps all brains marvellously select for us the most reliable channels according to our own sensory profile, and use our most reliable channels most often. Brains really are wonderful things.

Hyper-hypo sensory fluctuations

Let us consider now the reported experiences of people fluctuating between hyper- and hypo- states of sensitivity. Other people describe these as having a needle which swings between the two different states, so that one minute, they are over-sensitive to sounds, and the next minute, the needle swings violently and then they are under-sensitive.

For myself, I was convinced until recently that I did not have any hyper-hypo fluctuations. However, then I went shopping with my flatmate for my friend's birthday. We went into a shop which specialises in really smelly soaps and bath stuff. Knowing how incredibly insensitive my sense of smell is (it is the most hypo of all my senses; I probably smell two things per day) I thought I would be fine. In fact, I assumed I would cope much better than NTs with their normal sense of smell. However, in quite a short space of time in that shop, I felt myself becoming really agitated, and I nearly insisted on leaving, even though we had not yet decided on a present. I cannot really explain it, because it was not exactly painful, but it was somehow like torture. It was really bizarre because, although I get stressed, I do not usually have "melt-downs", but I felt as close to one there as I can ever remember. I actually wanted to have a tantrum in the middle of the shop. Luckily, I am socialised, so I refrained (just) from carrying out the tantrum. Another place I cannot stand is perfume departments. I have to hold my breath and move as fast as I can, like a swimmer diving underwater.

Perhaps the explanation is that autistic brains are not so good at modulating sensory input because none of the channels are constantly "on". For example, consider when you go into a night club. It is noisy. You go into the toilets, where it is quieter. You then go back out onto the dance floor. Exiting the toilets, you are hit by the loud noise and your ears take time to adjust to that again. Perhaps this is the autistic experience in everyday life; the same effect, but caused by a change of attention channel, rather than a change of environment. If this is true, my poor smell-interpreting part of my brain, which normally sits there doing nothing all day, in total quiet and being very bored in sensory-deprivation land, is occasionally bombarded with a ton of stimulation. It is like a monk who spends 99% of his life in solitary contemplation, suddenly being shouted at. No wonder I wanted to have a meltdown.

However, my Alexander teacher has a different theory. When I am having an Alexander lesson, I sometimes report sensations that other people would not notice (hypersensitive). My teacher might start by putting my head in the right place and then go on to realign my hips. My focus of concentration then shifts to my hips and I lose track of my head, which starts to loll around all over the place, and she will say, "I cannot leave you alone for a minute, can I?", and then she has to put my head back in the right place, before she can go on with my hips. It must be exhausting for the poor woman! She says it is not a random swinging of hyper to hypo states, because she controls which part of me is hypersensitive, as it is always the part she is working with at the time.

I think that possibly some people experiencing hyper-hypo fluctuations may be simply channel hopping and the fluctuating experience is mid-channel change. As I said, which channel I am on is largely involuntary and I guess this would be true for others too.

A speculative theory about Autism and ADD

As explained above, my channels are fairly stably set on "thinking" and "seeing", with the odd "hearing" coming in, usually prompted by human speech, but not so much by background sounds.

However, apart from thinking getting in the way of my hearing, I have good attention to writing this book, I have a very long attention span for studying/learning/revising, I can usually pay attention to a lecture without missing too much and I can usually stay relatively well focused on a conversation, as long as I can keep my thoughts to a minimum. Also, I do not tend to get distracted by any other sensory channel, except the thinking channel.

But, what if other people are different to me? What if their heads cycle them round all of their channels in turn, at a fast pace (like someone watching TV and channel-hopping with their remote control, the difference being, this channel-hopping is involuntary)? One of my more recent theories is this might explain Attention Deficit Disorder (ADD/ADHD). A person with ADD might have quickly hopping channels so that, when they are trying to listen to someone, their channel flips, involuntarily, and they miss a lot of what the person is saying. That would lead to the appearance of an attention deficit. In reality, it is not a lack of attention, because the attention is transferred onto another channel of sensory input, so actually, attention is being paid to something all the time. However, if the prime thing you should be doing is listening but your channels are hopping all over the place, you will not be able to pick up all of the auditory information and you will appear to be deficient in attention. Above, I explained that monoprocessing was a good defence to overload caused by gestalt perception. Quickly hopping channels could be another defence mechanism. It helps to ensure that you do not miss too much of what is going on around you in general, because each channel is given its own turn frequently. Furthermore, it is well-known that brains need sensory input, so that they do not undergo sensory deprivation (like the smell-interpretation part of my brain). Well, such channel-hopping would ensure a variety of sensory input to the brain, by cycling some/all of the channels in turn. However, the disadvantage is that from specific modalities, you are likely to miss an awful lot.

These theories about hyper-hypo fluctuating people and folk with ADD are purely my theories. I have not read them in any books. However, I am very convinced that monoprocessing is central to Autism and I have come up with these theories through talking to others about their experiences.

In conclusion, it is my view that how the core mechanisms of gestalt perception and monoprocessing take their effect differently in different individuals might account for the wide variation in experiences and abilities of people across the entire width and breadth of the autistic spectrum.

Cognitive Theories

There are three well-known cognitive theories of Autism: Theory of Mind, Weak Central Coherence and Executive Function. Theory of Mind concerns interpretation of mental states in oneself and others, which is what I will call mind-reading and what others call empathy. Weak Central Coherence is about focussing on details, rather than an overall picture. Executive Function is about the ability to organise yourself and your possessions in time and space.

In my opinion, these theories concern the consequences of gestalt perception and monoprocessing and are therefore less fundamental, lower order theories. But can gestalt perception and monoprocessing then explain these three cognitive theories? Yes, I think so. Let me explain…

Theory of Mind (and Theory of Autistic Mind)

According to current thinking regarding Theory of Mind, autistic people are less able to infer correctly the mental states of other folk. I agree with this general principle and I find it does cause problems in getting along with other people; particularly, if the other people do not realise there is a lack of Theory of Mind and take offence at things where none was intended.

So, how does Theory of Mind relate to gestalt perception and monoprocessing? Being mono-channelled, as opposed to multi-channelled, means I am always playing "catch-up" in conversations, and I am having to process pretty hard to follow the core of what is going on. This means I am generally in situations armed with an incomplete set of information, and hence, am less able to make good decisions. There is simply not enough processing time left to take in and analyse body language and facial expressions. To even begin to do this, I would have to try to switch off my ears when people talk to me and completely concentrate on what I am seeing.

Are you eating an orange?

Therefore, I would not be listening to the conversation, which is not practical. Hence, I have never been able to collect a repertoire of known facial expressions. This has the consequences that: (1) my facial expression might be doing the wrong thing; and (2) I may not correctly de-code someone else's facial expression.

Other people's faces give hints about their emotions and thoughts, and hence, I will never intuitively and effortlessly know what other people are thinking/feeling. Voilà, Theory of Mind difficulties.

On the topic of Theory of Mind, whilst I am not disputing that I have Theory of Mind difficulties, it can equally be said that most people have Theory of Autistic Mind difficulties when it comes to understanding me and other folk on the spectrum. Olga Bogdashina (2006) explains this really well. The concept of Theory of Mind is biased, because it is about understanding the thoughts and feelings of a *non-autistic* mind. So Theory of Mind tests are unfair. It is like an English person being tested on French culture.

I believe I have quite a good Theory of Autistic Mind, when it comes to understanding my fellow aspies and auties. My mind is quite simple and always needs all the relevant details. So, I try to provide others with all the relevant details. I do not communicate using complex codes/riddles/ambiguous ways. Instead, I communicate very literally and I do not use body language to do part of the work for me. I try really hard to say what I mean. This means I am very good at talking to children, teaching children and adults, communicating with foreign people in English and talking to autistic people. When I see that someone does not understand something, I look for a way to break the task/concept down into a list of rules or procedural steps that can be followed with as little interpretation on their part as possible. This works well for exam tutoring and I think it helps NTs as well as aspies and auties.

A while ago, I was discussing my hobby of "aspie-spotting" with one of my friends. By "aspie-spotting" I mean trying to work out whether members of the public are on the spectrum or not. They asked me, how can you tell who is an aspie? The most obvious response of someone on the autistic spectrum might be to walk up and directly ask the person whether or not they are an aspie. However, I prefer to use detective-work and try to figure it out. Most spectrum adults are unaware they are spectrum adults, so it would be pointless to ask them about something they did not know and probably painful for them too. My detail-oriented mind immediately started conjuring up a flow-chart with questions in boxes, one arrow pointing down one path if the answer was "yes" and another arrow/path if the answer was "no". I went home and wrote down forty-four different pointers (with explanations) to the kinds of things to look out for, trying to make it as clear and unambiguous as possible. That was tricky, because no two aspies are identical and probably no single aspie will fit all of my forty-four generalisations. And there was no standardised fool-proof recipe I could precisely give. For example, the ideal type of guidance would have been in the form: "if you spot between twenty-four and forty-four of these traits in someone, they definitely are an aspie, whereas if you only see twenty-three or less, they are an NT". However, aspie-spotting is not an exact science. After all, I do not conform to all autistic stereotypes.

In contrast, I do not think most NTs would have (or could have) answered my friend's question in this way. This highlights another fundamental difference between NT and aspie/autie thinking, which is fundamentally routed in gestalt perception. One of my NT friends once mentioned to me that she had suspected a TV quiz show contestant of being an aspie. When I asked her why she had thought that, she said she just "had a feeling" that the person may have been an aspie. Thus, my impression is that she would aspie-spot by gut instinct, whereas I am more rule-based and count up "clues" until I get enough for a conclusion. Although I had never written them out on paper before, it was very easy to come up with the forty-four pointers, because that is how I think.

Are you eating an orange?

Coming back to Theory of Mind, I find that NTs do not generally have good Theory of Autistic Mind abilities. Examples of NTs not understanding my words and deeds are scattered throughout this book. Why should I be regarded as a "good communicator" only if I can communicate well in the NT way (effectively the way of an alien culture)? I think that, if the tables were turned and the world was 99% autistic and 1% NT, those NTs would then be labelled as having a Triad of Impairments, and would definitely be seen as lacking a Theory of Mind.

I like this quote (by an autistic person):

"If I know that I do not understand people and I devote all this energy and effort to figuring them out, do I have more or less empathy than people who not only do not understand me, but who do not even notice that they do not understand me?" (Sinclair, 1989, cited in Bogdashina, 2006, p. 128).

After that brief diversion, let us now return to the other cognitive theories and look at how gestalt perception and monoprocessing can account for these.

Weak Central Coherence

The theory of Weak Central Coherence says that autistic people process parts, whilst NTs process wholes (Frith & Happé, 1994a). I question whether NTs really do process wholes or whether their processing of the most important parts merely gives that impression. One of my former colleagues has great central coherence and is fabulous about deciding upon overall strategies, but I am better with the details. The theory of gestalt perception implies that NTs also process parts but, using their good "brain sieves", they will process only the most important parts. Their brains then fill in the rest with their imagination and their good ability to generalise from previous knowledge. This technique gives them a good idea of what the whole picture is.

Autistic people, without "brain sieves", process the parts which randomly get their attention, which may not be the most important parts. So, NTs can take their overall view and very quickly zoom into the parts which require additional attention, going from the whole to the most relevant details. In contrast, autistic people need to laboriously piece together all of the details, before they can even start to see the big picture emerging.

I experience this a lot when reading complex technical documents. When reading a technical document, I have noticed that some people can look quickly at the drawings to get a good overall view and then jump to the part in the text which is talking about a particular bit they need to know about. In five minutes, they can have an overview of the document and know the pertinent facts of the matter at hand. In contrast, I find I have to read the whole document from the beginning to the end. I have tried to speed up my reading by using this quicker method, but it does not work for me. I usually get very confused because of lacking a good overall view and the information which, for me, needs to be explicit and which I cannot just guess or generalise from previous knowledge. Usually, I then have to revert to my slow and plodding way, reading the entire document.

When an autistic person thinks something, because they have started with the details and consciously formed the conclusion, they are more likely to be able to explain their reasoning. This is supported by Olga Bogdashina (2006), who explained that the autistic people who were able to solve Theory of Mind problems could give a precise reasoning, whereas NTs would know the answer but could not explain how they knew it. So, if you ask an autistic person to justify something, they then just remember how they worked out the conclusion and can explain it to you.

In contrast, NT-thinking is intuitive (gut instinct). NTs have very complex brains that give them an immediate overall picture of a situation. For example, they talk in broad concepts like: "I just have a feeling that X is Y…". I have a theory that NTs sometimes do not even know why they have that feeling/belief. I think their brains are doing similar steps to mine, but on an unconscious level and all that gets presented to their conscious mind is the final conclusion. This is a great labour-saving technique for them.

When NTs try to justify their gut feelings, they have to *consciously* work from the overall picture towards the details, which is artificial for them, because their conclusion was formed unconsciously. I think this sometimes leads to difficulties.

An example of this was I was once told at a work assessment that I was not professional enough. I was really bewildered and dismayed about this. My understanding of being professional was being polite, working hard, meeting deadlines and generally doing your work as well as possible. I was already doing all of this. I did not understand what I could possibly do to become more professional. It did not occur to me that my understanding of "professional" might be different from someone else's, or to ask for a definition.

A few months later (coincidentally) I started learning the Alexander Technique and my posture consequently improved. At my next assessment, I was complimented on my increased professionalism. I was really surprised. Nothing had changed in my mental attitude to my work. I was still being polite, working hard, meeting deadlines and generally doing my work as well as possible. The only change I could think of was my posture. When I explained this, my boss seemed to me to be surprised. He may have thought that I had made a mental change, not a physical one.

In hindsight, I understand that Neurotypical people rely heavily on things like body language and facial expression as a clue to what is going on in someone's head. It is quite possible that in many cases, this will lead to correct assumptions being drawn. For example, if a Neurotypical employee does not sit up straight and folds their arms in a defensive posture, this might mean that the person cannot be bothered about their work and does not have a professional attitude. However, people on the spectrum tend not to have the mental space to be able to take in body language along with the overload of other incoming information. Therefore their own body language might not accurately reflect their mental attitude. It therefore seems likely to me that if an employee who is on the spectrum exhibits negative body language, it is possible for someone else to draw an incorrect conclusion about their mental attitude to their work.

In my case, there was no profound fundamental change in my attitude to my work; just the uprightness of my spine.

Personally, I would have found it more helpful to have had it explained to me that I should change my posture, rather than that I should become more professional. I would certainly have been less confused.

However, changing my posture was a small detail, whereas becoming more professional was the big picture. If NTs more naturally see the big picture, perhaps they do not so easily see the details, in which case it would have been difficult for big-picture people to understand and explain to me on the level of the details, what I needed to do. If NTs sometimes do not know how the big picture breaks up into the small details, whereas aspies and auties need the details, you can see how difficult it is for spectrum-NT communication to work.

Executive Function

Executive Function is about the ability to organise yourself and your possessions in time and space. Since it concerns many different things, it is a difficult one to quantify. However, I most notice my Executive Function issues when I am trying to be quick. For example, when travelling and trying to get off a plane or train,

Are you eating an orange?

I am usually the last one to manage to get all my stuff together and leave. I am usually the last one to be ready after work to go to the pub, even though I am often hurrying. My poor Executive Function was really apparent when camping as part of a kayak holiday. It was me who spent an extra 30% longer trying to scramble out of the kayak, scramble across rocks and pack up the tent. It was me who could not quite stuff all my things into the small hatch in the kayak and needed extra help, whereas other people managed to carry extra cooking equipment too. It was me who could not work out which kayak belonged to my friend, when asked to put something in their kayak. It was me who was the last one up, organised, in the kayak and ready to go the next morning. It was also me who struggled with the rudder system for altering the direction of my kayak depending on the wind direction and me who ended up getting towed by the trip leader. It is not a big deal, each individual thing, but overall it makes me slower, which can be embarrassing and stressful. My Executive Function difficulties also make some apparently "simple" jobs quite hard, for example, waitressing.

Relating this back to gestalt perception and monoprocessing, many tasks which involve Executive Function also involve multi-channel processing, which is obviously a problem for the mono-channelled. Single-channel processing is slower than multi-channel processing and therefore, we are slower at doing such tasks. We therefore have worse Executive Function.

Hence, I believe gestalt perception and monoprocessing can account quite adequately for the three main cognitive theories: Theory of Mind, Weak Central Coherence, and Executive Function.

Communication

What is Communication?

Bogdashina (2005) teaches us that communication is the transmission and reception of information and that the necessary elements for communication to take place are:

- A sender who transmits information
- A receiver who receives information
- Something to transmit/communicate about (an awareness of needs, ideas)
- Communicative intent (desire to affect the receiver's mind)
- A medium of transmission (a means of communication shared by both participants).

Communication can be linguistic or non-linguistic. Non-linguistic means of communication include body language, facial expressions, gestures, pictures/symbols. Linguistic means of communication are sign language, spoken language and written language (Bogdashina, 2005).

Did you know that language and communication are not the same thing? I had not really thought about this before, but I think it is pretty cool. Frith & Happé (1994b, p. 97) explain this, stating:

"A language is a grammar-governed representational system. By contrast, communication is a process in which one person alters the physical environment of another in such a way that the other constructs internal representations similar to those in the head of the first. Clearly this process of altering internal states is independent from the means used. While we commonly use words in order to communicate, Sperber & Wilson (1986) claim that words and sentences are just one type of tool which can be employed".

Thus, communication can be defined as a process of altering mental states, whilst language is just *one* means of achieving communication.

Other non-language means of communication include gestures, mime, gaze and other types of non-verbal communication. You have only to watch "Wallace and Gromit" (a children's animation) to realise that Gromit (a dog) communicates brilliantly and very expressively without ever speaking. Since language and communication are different, "communication is possible without language, but can also fail in the presence of good language skills" (Frith & Happé, 1994b, p. 97-98).

As stated earlier, communication is one of the Triad of Impairments (Wing, 1997). Wing summarises the communication difficulty as:

"Impairment of communication affecting both comprehension and use of speech, vocal intonation and body language varies from no communication to fluent, grammatical speech that is used mainly or only to talk about special interests. Communication problems are obvious among those who are more disabled but tend to be more subtle among the more able people." (Wing, 2004, p. 543).

There, that is quite enough "impairment" talk.

Literal Communication

Autistic people generally have a literal communication style. Unfortunately, the rest of the world generally does not and this can cause major problems and misunderstandings.

If the meaning of a message is obvious and it contradicts the literal words, NT adults only pay attention to the meaning and ignore the literal. NT children are also more interested in intentions than words. It is difficult for them to pay attention to the literal form of a message when the intention is clear (Beal & Flavell,

Communication

1984, cited in Frith & Happé, 1994b). This shows the precedence of communication over language as a feature of normal communication (Frith & Happé, 1994b).

In contrast, with autistic people, the literal interpretation is sometimes the only one available because, due to a lack of mind-reading skills, the intention might be unclear. Autistic people hear things first on a literal level and then have to work hard to "translate" the meaning out of it. Since, due to gestalt perception, we are bombarded with more information than we can process, our brains are pretty busy and the time-delay between hearing the literal and working out the meaning is sometimes obvious to others, even if we do work out the correct meaning in the end.

An example of this is how people respond to questions which start with negatives. It is actually very illogical. When I was a child and my Mum asked: "Don't you want to play outside?", my reply was "yes" but I meant "yes I do not want to play outside". In case my logic is not obvious to you, I will explain my thinking.

"Don't you want to play outside?" = "Do you not want to play outside?" = "Is it true that you do not want to play outside?". So, if I did not want to play outside, the answer is "Yes, it is true that I do not want to play outside" = "yes I do not want to play outside" = (shortened reply) "Yes".

Therefore, if I did want to play outside, I would have said "no" and meant "no, I do not *not* want to play outside" = "I do want to play outside". However, this is the opposite way round to how people normally interpret a question starting with a negative. Also, the fact that I worked out logically how to answer the question, as opposed to listening and copying other people, is a significant difference compared to NTs.

Autistic people may fail to use and understand lies, jokes, metaphors, faux pas and deception (Baron-Cohen, 1997, cited in Dennis et al., 2001), which are all types of non-literal communication. Difficulties in understanding indirect requests and hints can be explained as immediate effects of a lack of Theory of Mind (Frith & Happé, 1994b).

In one study, aspies performed significantly more poorly than controls on indirect pragmatic interpretation questions (Martin & McDonald, 2004). Specifically, aspies had difficulty with the pragmatic interpretation of ironic jokes and were more likely to conclude that the protagonist was lying, rather than telling an ironic joke. Martin & McDonald concluded this showed an inability to use the social context to interpret the pragmatic meaning in conversation. They state that although aspies often possess intact language abilities, they can still have deficits in pragmatic language (use of language in a social context).

Luke Jackson sums up the problem with indirect communication perfectly:

"Non-AS people say things they don't mean, miss out things they do mean, do all sorts of strange things with their faces which apparently change the meaning of their words - and they say AS people are odd!" (Jackson, 2002b, p. 108).

We aspies and auties *do* learn things (being on the spectrum involves a steep on-going learning curve), but we are more likely to learn through rote-learning a rule or applying logic, rather than through observation and imitating others. Actually, I frequently think that I mostly learn through making social mistakes and the consequent embarrassment! However, our learning is often impeded by the way NTs give us feedback. Luke explains:

"To say 'If you do so-and-so… then it makes me feel sad and I do not like feeling sad so please do not do it again' is fine and simple to understand…but adults and people in general usually go on about 'How do you think this makes me feel?' and 'Do you not care about us?' and 'You are so selfish' and I still end up wondering exactly what the point is that they are trying to make!" (Jackson, 2002b, p. 108).

Luke's Mum, in contrast, uses a much better method of communicating with Luke:

"Mum is very blunt with me and I think that shocks other people. She will say, 'Luke shut up for five minutes'…This does not offend me one bit." (Jackson, 2002b, p. 102-103).

Literal misunderstandings can lead to confusion on both sides. Liane Holliday Willey explains:

"For the first several years of our marriage, Tom had no idea I was misconstruing his thoughts because, from his perspective, he had been clear and articulate. He was left to think I had just failed to listen to him while I was left wondering why he did not care that he had confused me so." (Holliday Willey, 1999, p. 63).

I have been told that I "should not expect the rest of the world to change and communicate in a more literal way for me". However, this seems awfully unfair to me, because if people just said what they meant, my communication problems would be vastly reduced. I cannot alter my understanding or vastly increase my comprehension abilities beyond the point I have now attained at this stage in my life. However, NTs can adapt their communication style. One of the hardest things is that often, neither party to the conversation will be able to realise even that there is a literal communication problem, even when the problem is really major or frequent. The aspie/autie assumes that the NT has said what they meant and does not know why the NT is angry. The NT assumes the aspie/autie has understood them but it ignoring what they said.

Here follow some examples of literal communication problems:

Are you eating an orange?

Example 1

Luke Jackson (writing when thirteen years old) gives a beautiful example, which demonstrates a number of areas of difficulty:

"Me sitting daydreaming... All of a sudden, a shadow looms over me. I glance up and see the formidable form of the teacher. He towers over me, arms folded, the pungent mixture of sweat and after-shave filling my nostrils. I await the moment when he pounces. "Jackson," he suddenly booms, "Would you care to tell us exactly where you are?"

"Class E2, Sir," I respond as quickly and politely as possible.

"Are you trying to be smart?" he snarls, his face reddening with anger.

"Yes, Sir," I reply, "of course I am trying to be smart." I think to myself, "Surely that is why we are at school?" I breathe an inward sigh of relief, presuming he will now leave me alone, but when I look up, I see I am wrong.

His eyes are bulging, he is breathing fast and hard and his face is the colour of a beetroot. "Jackson, I will not, I repeat not, tolerate such insolence. You can pull your socks up or get to the headmaster's office."

Now when I was younger I would have bent down and done just that, pulled my socks up... However, I smile to myself inwardly. "Ha", I think, "I know this one - it means get on with your work, not pull your socks up." Grinning with delight at the fact that I have finally understood, I pick up my pen and start to write. Well you would have thought that that was the end but it seems not!

"This is no laughing matter and how dare you ignore me when I am speaking to you". Eh? Speaking? I wasn't aware he was! His rage seems to have been replaced by simmering anger that he has managed to suppress only to allow it to erupt at a later date. His face is like thunder. "See me after class for an hour's detention," he hisses in my ear in a menacing manner." (Jackson, 2002b, p. 103-104).

I fully understand Luke's "grin of delight", because I feel the same on the rare occasions where I do grasp someone's (to me) convoluted meaning.

Example 2

"...when I was working out in the gym some pretty-looking woman came up to me and said 'Are you seeing anyone?' My immediate reaction was, is she referring to me as if I am blind? I answered by saying, 'I am not visually impaired, I see people all the time, it is natural for human beings to see people.' Then I started going into detail like I normally do such as talking about the iris, pupil, conjunctiva and optic nerves. She got very offended and at that point, she walked off. I automatically thought, well, that is very rude of her and I never saw her again." (Kamlesh Pandya, writing in Edmonds & Beardon, 2008, p. 79).

Example 3

Donna Williams did not consider she was doing anything wrong in writing graffiti on a school wall after promising she would never again write different graffiti on Parliament House (Williams, 1998).

Example 4

My friend, on taking a lasagne out of her freezer, read the packet, on which was written "Co-operative Beef Lasagne". She turned to her partner and asked: "how can this beef lasagne be more co-operative than other beef lasagnes?" Actually, the lasagne was from the "Co-Op" supermarket, and the word "Co-operative" was being used as a Trade Mark on the packaging. I think the mental image of a beef lasagne taking part in team building exercises and co-operating nicely is hilarious! My friend and I had a good laugh about this.

Are you eating an orange?

It seems to me that some of these non-literal language interpretation problems are a direct consequence of failure to take the overall context into account. Luke did not take the context of the angry teacher into account and missed the sarcasm. My friend did not notice the indications on the packaging that "co-operative" was used as a Trade Mark and she also did not imagine another interpretation once she realised that a beef lasagne is not usually something which co-operates.

However, Donna's example was the result of poor mind-reading skills (lack of Theory of Mind). She did not understand the intention behind what she was being told not to do (not to write graffiti anywhere). She only understood the literal words.

Example 5

This example is from my own life.

(On a train)

A senior colleague sits opposite me. He is using his mobile phone. I start peeling an orange. He looks at me.

My colleague: "Are you eating an orange?"

Me: "Yes."

My colleague: "I can smell it."

Me (thinking: Huh? He does not need to use his nose to know that I am eating an orange): "I can see it."

Five minutes of silence, during which my colleague goes back to his mobile phone, giving me some spare time to do some hard thinking.

Communication

Me: "Are you trying to tell me you do not think I should be eating an orange on this train?"

My colleague (blushing and stammering in embarrassment): "Of course I would never dream of telling you what to do, but if you are really forcing me to express an opinion and twisting my arm, I would have to say I do find it rather smelly and offensive."

I was stunned that anyone would try to express such a simple sentiment in such a complicated way. I was more than a little amused at the huge embarrassment this NT apparently had about communicating directly.

I must emphasise how incredibly confused I was by my colleague's utterance. I was not trying to embarrass him, I was simply trying to understand what he was saying. In this instance, it was lucky that I was not doing anything for the five minutes, so I had time to quietly and calmly try to work out his meaning. But in most interactions, such time and calm is not usually available, and I shudder to think how many other instances there must have been in which I have completely missed the communication.

In hindsight, I find this whole conversation really very funny. I find it helps to be able to laugh about such situations and miscommunications; it is a much more useful response than being depressed about them and withdrawing from the world. Me and my aspie/autie friends help each other to laugh at our failures to communicate, our misunderstandings and the differences between how we think and how most people do, instead of taking it all too seriously.

Small Talk

From the autistic perspective, communication = exchange of information. The autistic attitude is often: "If there is no practical information to exchange, why waste time talking?" (Attwood,

2007, p. 208). One of my aspie friends takes this attitude; he only talks when he has something significant to say.

However, Frith explains that for NTs, communication is more than a mere information exchange and serves an ulterior purpose. For example, talking about the weather can confirm a social alliance and promote a future social interchange. Frith says: "Communication appears to be intimately connected with our human ability to attribute intention to ourselves and others and to use this ability in order to influence social relationships" (Frith, 1998, p. 56). She concludes that communication is more similar to mind-reading than it is to encoding and decoding information. A consequence of the "communication = exchange of information" attitude is that the conversation can dry up (Frith, 1998).

Liane learned in her drama classes to think of language as "more than a means for expressing simple needs" (Holliday Willey, 1999, p. 30). Note, she *learned* this, it was not something she knew instinctively.

Another example is Cornish's (aspie) views on small talk:

"... I was waiting to be served in my local paper shop. An elderly lady was stood next to me and insisted that I gave her five minutes of my time, while she went on about the obvious state of the weather. Come on lady... I've just driven down here... I've seen what the weather's like... Why do the NTs insist on stating the bleeding obvious at every available opportunity?" (Edmonds & Beardon, 2008, p. 154).

I have to admit here that I am on the autistic side of things in this point. I feel frequently stumped at not knowing what to say in the way of small talk. However, I have started to experiment with saying some complete random waffle about nothing very much. The preliminary results are promising, in that I have had some friendly replies. In many situations though, I feel that I have to be the one to speak first, which I do not quite understand. It could be that I give off strange "autistic" vibes which perhaps make me look different, threatening or unfriendly, so I have to make the first overture to demonstrate that I am not any of these things.

My experiments in small talk have given me some considerable amusement. In one particular week on entering the office, I met one of my bosses in the lift. It had been raining, and I was looking drippy and dishevelled and was carrying my wet, fluorescent cycling jacket and rucksack. This is never a good start. But anyway, at the time, I had disclosed my aspie-status officially, which gave me a bit of confidence that whatever mistakes I was committing (and about to commit) might be received a bit more understandingly. My boss initiated some small talk about the weather. He informed me that it was looking like rain for the weekend as well. I said: "oh dear, were you planning a grand barbecue", to which he replied that he was not. I desperately tried to think of some indoor activities: "Oh, never mind, you could go ten-pin bowling or ice-skating," I said. Good grief! This, said to my boss, who was serious, suited, profit-oriented, and probably did not have ice-skating as a hobby! I am still chuckling about this episode now.

Liane says that you should have different conversational approaches, depending on the status of the person you are speaking with (Holliday Willey, 2001). She sets out two examples on page 172 of the style of communicating that is appropriate with three different status groups (authority figures, casual acquaintances and close friends and family). My experience was a very definite result of failing to do this. This is actually stuff that I knew, but the problem was with needing to react quickly in the heat of the moment. Still, I think that if I have to be bad at small talk, I may as well be really bad at it!

Effects of Theory of Mind on Communication

In the Autism literature, "empathy" is defined in various different ways.

87

Are you eating an orange?

The affective approach defines empathy as "an observer's emotional response to the affective state of another" (Baron-Cohen & Wheelwright, 2004). Baron-Cohen & Wheelwright additionally specify that the emotional response must be appropriate. For example, being pleased when someone is upset is an emotional response to the affective state of another, but should not be defined as having empathy because it is not an appropriate response to their sadness.

The cognitive approach defines empathy as having a Theory of Mind. That is, setting aside one's own current perspective, attributing a mental state to the other person and then inferring the likely content of their mental state, given the experience of that person (Baron-Cohen & Wheelwright, 2004).

Frith & Happé (1994b) believe that many communication problems are a result of lack of Theory of Mind. Autistic people can supply information, but do not take account of the listener's needs in supplying that information (Perner et al, 1989, cited in Frith & Happé, 1994b). This lack of ability to accurately infer the mental states of others affects communication both when the autistic person is the speaker and when they are the receiver. Frith & Happé (1994b) believe that the language of autistic people is peculiar due to lack of insight into other people's minds.

I find being told that "autistic people do not have empathy" is untrue and insulting. I will use "empathy" to mean "taking account of someone else's viewpoint". I will use "mind-reading" or "Theory of Mind" to mean what is often described in the literature as "empathy": the intuitive ability to know what someone is thinking and feeling. Autistic people only actually have a problem with "mind-reading" - not knowing about someone else's feelings because we have not been told what they are explicitly. We are fully capable of being empathic, provided that we are told what the other person's viewpoint is, in a suitable way for us.

Communication

Luke Jackson expresses the mind-reading problem very well:

"I am always being shouted at for not thinking of what others may be feeling, but I am sorry to say that I often do not. I have great difficulty thinking what others may be feeling and, even when they tell me, they are never clear enough." (Jackson, 2002b, p. 108-109).

Luke's Mum explains that Luke presumes other people know what he is thinking and feeling (Jackson, 2004, p. 59).

Many tests for Theory of Mind (mind-reading abilities) have now been conducted with autistic people. The first and most famous test is called the "Sally Ann" test (Baron-Cohen, Leslie, & Frith, 1985), which is as follows. Some test subjects (children) watch the following scenario. Sally puts a marble in a first box and then leaves the room. Ann moves the marble into a second box. Sally comes back into the room. The children are asked "where will Sally look for the marble?" 80% of the Autistic children said Sally would look for the marble in the second box, where *they* knew that it was. These children failed to take account of Sally's knowledge (the marble being in the first box) being different from their own knowledge. In contrast, 86% of the children with Down's Syndrome said Sally would look in the first box.

Failing to realise a difference between one's own knowledge and another person's knowledge is lack of Theory of Mind, on the most basic level. A curious point is that 20% of the autistic children did answer correctly.

Following on from this test, other tests have confirmed that many autistic people can pass Theory of Mind tests (see Bowler, 1992). However, even the high functioning autistic people who pass Theory of Mind tests may not actually have a Theory of Mind, as their passing could be due to "compensatory learning in the presence of a severe deficit" (Frith, 1991, p. 21). Autistic people may acquire a conscious Theory of Mind, whilst still lacking an intuitive mentalising ability (Hill & Frith, 2003). Autistic children who correctly answer Theory of Mind questions give eloquent explanations, unlike most NT children (Happé, 1995, cited in Bogdashina, 2006). To me, this is evidence that the correct response was worked out logically by the autistic children and intuitively by the NT children.

I know that if I was given the Sally-Ann test, I would get the answer right. However, I would definitely get there by logic, using a series of facts and steps. I know that Sally's knowledge might be different than my knowledge (learned through experience in childhood). I know that if she is out of the room, she cannot see what happens to the marble in the room. I know that when she leaves the room, she will know the marble is in the first box. I know that people remember things and so she will remember the location of the marble is in the first box. Therefore, when she comes back, if she is not told any differently, I know that she will think the marble is still in the first box. However, fascinatingly, when I described the Sally-Ann test to my NT friend, she said she would "just know" what Sally thought, without having to work through all these steps.

This all suggests NTs may have a Theory of Mind "module" in their brains, which gives then an *intuitive* mentalising ability, which autistic people do not have. However, through logic, some high functioning autistic people can also come to the right conclusion, albeit through a completely different process.

The clearest way I have to illustrate the difference between having this Theory of Mind "module"/intuitive mentalising abilities, and by not having this, is by the following example.

I and other colleagues had signed up to go to a conference. Some weeks previously, all attendees had received an e-mail, confirming our attendance. One colleague sent a group e-mail:

Communication

"Am I the only person going to the conference? I am the only attendee listed in the diary."

I started a reply:
"Dear Colleague, no, I am going, so are many others".

I then remembered the confirmatory e-mail. I added to my draft reply:
"I am forwarding you an e-mail, which lists the attendees."

I searched through my inbox, found the e-mail, and attached it. I saw that the address line included my colleague's name.

"Strange", I thought. "Has my colleague forgotten this e-mail?"

"Probably not".

"Why is he asking a question to which he already knows the answer?"

The truth slowly dawned:

"Oh, my colleague was *not* asking a question, he was chastising us for not having put our attendance in the diary". I deleted my draft reply.

This took about four minutes. I asked another colleague about their reaction to this e-mail. My other colleague had *instantly* realised that the e-mail was a criticism, and not a question. I felt annoyed that I had wasted so much time.

I discussed this with my cousin (NT), who imagined what her thought processes would have been in the same situation. Part of our thought processes were the same. My cousin would have stored knowledge about the conference in a "database" in her head (existence of conference, date, who is attending) and when my colleague's e-mail was received a few weeks later, she would have immediately accessed this database. I had done this; when I read the e-mail, I immediately recalled the existence of the conference and the knowledge that a large group was attending. There was no delay in accessing this knowledge.

However, in parallel with my cousin's database of conference information, she would also have kept a database of knowledge about what other people's knowledge about the conference was. I had not done that. If I had not found the e-mail and noticed my colleague's name on the addressee list, *nothing* would have prompted me to realise that my colleague already knew the answer to his own question. Hence, the difference was that I lacked a parallel monitoring of other people's knowledge about the conference, in addition to my own knowledge.

Therefore, my cousin (NT) automatically keeps track of not only her knowledge of a given situation, but other people's knowledge, in a parallel database running simultaneously in her head. So, if she needs a relevant fact about other people's knowledge, it is easily accessible. She has not made any effort to start the database, maintain it, or access its knowledge. In contrast, I keep track of my knowledge about situations, but not other people's. So, if I need to know someone else's viewpoint, I have to go through a series of steps. First, I need to realise the situation requires me to know their knowledge and to check whether their actions/words make sense in the context of their knowledge. Sometimes, people are not being straightforward and direct and so their knowledge might be different than what they are saying it is. Then, I have to access my general memory and try to remember instances that I learned something and to think whether they also had access to that information or not. An important point is this is searching my whole memory bank and not a handy parallel database. This is difficult and time-consuming, so it is easier to rely on what I can find out in the present moment.

This raises an important point. In general, the explanation for autistic people not having Theory of Mind is that we do not realise other people have different knowledge than us. But I do not remember a time, even when I was very little, when I did not know that other people have different knowledge to me. Under no situations is that the stumbling block for me. In contrast, the easiest way (the "path of least resistance", as my physics friend would say) to understand a situation is to believe what people are telling me. In many cases, this is a sensible short-cut, because normally what people say is a pretty good guide to what they know. If I had to have a ten-minute think for every utterance people made, to check whether what they said made sense with what I could painstakingly recall they might know, I would never get anywhere. However, like many short-cuts, it will not work in all situations, for example the above example, in which my colleague was being deliberately indirect, by asking a question to which he already knew the answer.

It is not just autistic people who make short-cuts in their lives. Our modern world is so complex, we all have to make short-cuts, whenever we do not have the time to acquire the knowledge we need. We do not have the time to become an expert on which brand of any particular goods is better than another brand. You cannot become a jewellery expert before choosing a diamond ring. One short-cut people often make is "expensive = good", using the general rule that "you get what you pay for". This often works, so people use it. But this leads to the situation where marketers can exploit this, because you can increase the price of something and it actually becomes more popular!

NTs make short cuts for similar reasons, when judging someone on their body language and communication style. My NT cousin explained that such assumptions are justified because, for most people, these things would indeed be good indicators of someone's mental attitude. It seems to me that these assumptions are good for NTs, as they allow them to make speedy judgements that are correct most of the time. However, in the 1% of the autistic population, these judgements will often be wrong. So, for NTs, these assumptions "work" 99% of the time, which is acceptable to them. If the consequences of the 1% of incorrect assumptions were evenly distributed throughout the whole population, I agree that being wrong only 1% of the time is fair enough. However, this is not the case. Whilst I can understand that short-cuts are great, the unfairest aspect of this is that the autistic 1% has to bear the brunt of these wrong assumptions for 99% of their lives.

Further examples of the effects of Theory of Mind on communication from my life include that I frequently go into too much detail when asked a simple question. To the question "how are you?" my natural response is to answer it, honestly, and in detail. It is remarkable how difficult I still find it to remember just to say "fine" and that I am being asked the question for politeness, and not because the other person wants to know how I am. About two years ago, without knowing this particular social convention, when my colleague asked "how are you?", I paused, considered, frowned a little and replied honestly: "middling-to-crap". I was most bemused that my colleague started laughing.

To the question from someone else: "do you need the fridge?", I replied that first I was needing the sink, but after using the sink I was going to use the kettle once and the fridge twice, once to fetch and put back the milk. Partway into that explanation I did realise that a simple "yes" would have sufficed, but then I found I was enjoying working out how many times I would use each bit of equipment, so I carried on regardless. However, I am sure this was not the expected reply.

Considering again the definition of "empathy", various definitions in the literature include:

1)   having an appropriate emotional response to another person's affective state;

2)   being able to take account of someone else's viewpoint (which might be different than your own) to correctly understand a situation; or

3)   having an intuitive Mind-Reading ability.

In my opinion, if we take the third definition (intuitive Mind-Reading ability), then I agree that we lack this ability. But, if we take the second definition (taking account of someone else's viewpoint), then we are not lacking in this ability because we are potentially able to do it using logic, although sometimes the viewpoint will need to be explicitly explained to us.

I postulate that "empathy" and "mind-reading" are actually two different skills. It certainly should help your empathy skills if you are able to mind-read, because understanding someone else's viewpoint can be easier if you are able to do this intuitively rather than having to work it out logically. However, in my experience, it is quite possible to have mind-reading skills but still very little empathy. I have met many people like this. NTs do not understand where I am coming from alarmingly often, because we are from two different cultures and they do not understand mine and are largely unaware of it. Olga Bogdashina describes this as NTs lacking "a Theory of Autistic Mind" (Bogdashina, 2006).

In my opinion, many communication problems are directly caused by autistic people being a minority group. The fact that NTs may have intuitive mind-reading abilities does not mean that they can literally mind-read. It is very much more difficult, for both NTs and autistic people, to be able to predict another person's thoughts and feelings if *you* are not the same as *them*. I suppose even for NTs with their sophisticated intuitive mind-reading skills, often having empathy just comes down to obeying the ethical maxim "do unto others as you would have done unto you". In other words, if you do not like something, you can hypothesise that someone else will not like it either. All well and good, but this relies on you actually being similar people. I remember once answering someone's mobile phone for them. This person was not happy about this and very nicely asked me not to do it again in future. When I later discussed this with a friend, he seemed to think at first that I had been discourteous for picking up the mobile and invading his privacy. However, he then asked me whether I would have wanted someone else to answer my mobile phone in a similar situation. I said: "yes, I would consider it very helpful to take a message". My friend then understood why I had done it and he realised that I had not acted out of lack of consideration for others. I had, in fact, done to others as I would have had done to me, which is the best that anyone can do. The trouble was, I was unusual in my mobile phone answering preferences, and I did not know this at the time.

In my experience, the advantage NTs have with their intuitive mind-reading skills does not work very well when they are interacting with autistic people, as their intuition can be based upon the other person being similar to them.

An example of this in my life was recently. I made a plan with my friend to go out for dinner after work one day, so that we could catch up with each other. At the last minute, my friend changed the nature of the dinner (just two of us became a big group), the reason for the dinner (a farewell dinner for another girl) and the location (the departing girl's favourite restaurant, which was fancy, noisy, and not suitable for my GF-CF diet). In this instance, my friend (being a sociable and flexible NT) did not take into account (1) I do not like last minute changes of plan; (2) for me, a group of people is entirely different and much more difficult than a one-to-one dinner; (3) I genuinely wanted to catch up properly with my friend instead of having a big group banter; and (4) that not being able to order anything other than an expensive and insubstantial starter course would make me unhappy. Since these changes did not bother my friend, she inferred (incorrectly) they would not bother me. I decided not to go and made an excuse. Her intuitive mind-reading abilities did not work in this case, when she was confronted with a different type of mind. The communication broke down because she could not infer my point of view and I did not feel confident in making too much of a fuss about these things that I thought would not have bothered other people.

Therefore, if empathy and mind-reading skills are different, and if some NTs have mind-reading skills but no empathy, then it seems reasonable that some autistic people can have empathy, but no mind-reading skills. I believe I have quite a good Theory of Autistic Mind when it comes to understanding and communicating with my fellow aspies and auties. For the same reason that NTs can predict other NTs better than autistic people, I can sometimes predict autistic people better than NTs. I know how I would feel in a particular situation and so I can imagine that they would feel something similar.

I am not alone in being good at getting on with other autistic people. Kamlesh Pandya is an aspie who got a job working with low-functioning autistic people. He reports:

"When other staff worked with the same service users, a lot of them were physically targeted and could not work with certain service users. Female staff often had their hair pulled, faeces thrown at them, or they got bitten; whereas with me, it was the opposite, I rarely got targeted in the three years." (Edmonds & Beardon, 2008, p. 78).

Smukler (2005) makes the point that even in the profession of Autism, there may be no empathy between NTs and autistic people and that the dominant "deficit-oriented" approach of the Autism-field is to blame. He says that:

"Characterising those with Autism labels as "unfortunate", privileges him [Baron-Cohen], as well as his presumably non-autistic readers, as fortunate, creating unbridgeable distance and precluding real empathy." (Smukler, 2005, p. 20).

Are you eating an orange?

This is another example of NTs having mind-reading skills but no empathy. Smukler is also critical of Baron-Cohen's definition of Theory of Mind as being "one of the quintessential abilities that makes us human" (Baron-Cohen, 2001, cited in Smukler, 2005, p. 17). This dehumanising approach makes it harder for NTs to have empathy with us.

Liane makes the point that NTs:

"are not always certain how to respond to us, how to talk to us, look at us, work with us, be with us. I find myself wondering if that might be the case not only because they find us complex, but also because we find them equally as fuddled. Both groups seem woefully unable to conceptualize an accurate theory of the other's mind." (Holliday Willey, 2001, p. 155)

A friend of a friend quite obviously feels uncomfortable around me and although we are both nice people and we both try, we do not find a way to connect with each other. I think she feels uncomfortable because she senses that I am lacking in some (to her) "essentially human" attributes.

Inferences

Understanding and using language is more than a mere decoding procedure. Much of what we need to understand is not directly stated, written or depicted, but involves constructing meaning through an integration of knowledge and language by a process of inferencing (Dennis, Lazenby & Lockyer, 2001). Autistic people can have difficulty understanding information that is not directly stated. Therefore, even if an autistic person has heard all of the words of a sentence correctly, this does not guarantee that they have understood the sentence.

Inferencing is like building bridges between different pieces of information to make a coherent whole. If you have two facts, you might be able to infer a third fact. Sometimes inferencing involves inferring a mental state of another person. An example of this is: I am late to meet my friend; people can feel angry if they are kept waiting; therefore my friend might be angry because I am late. Other types of inferencing have nothing to do with mental states. An example of this is: all cats have four legs; Sooty is a cat; therefore Sooty has four legs.

Inferencing and the ability to abstract context-dependent meanings are important for good communication (Norbury & Bishop, 2002). Inferencing is frequently described as an area of difficulty for autistic people. Mental state inferencing is said to be particularly difficult (Dennis et al., 2001).

Norbury et al. (2002) compared a group of autistic children to other groups of children with particular language impairments, and found that the autistic group performed more poorly than other groups on questions requiring inferences, particularly gap-filling inferences.

A study by Dennis et al. (2001) found that high functioning autistic children could identify multiple meanings for ambiguous words. However, they failed to infer what mental state verbs implied in context, to make inferences about social scripts and to understand metaphors. Since recognising ambiguity was easier for this group than understanding metaphors, the problem appears to be with the intentionality of the utterance, rather than because there were multiple possible interpretations.

Jolliffe & Baron-Cohen (1999) conducted three experiments which found:

1)   autistic people were less likely to use sentence context spontaneously to provide context-appropriate pronunciation of a homograph;

2)   autistic people were less likely to select the most coherent inference from alternatives (choosing the sentence which best filled a gap in a story); and

3)   autistic people were less able to use context to interpret an auditorily presented ambiguous sentence.

The results of experiments 1 and 3 indicate that autistic people find it difficult to take the overall context into account. The result of experiment 2 indicates a deficit in integrating information and/ or an impaired knowledge base.

For myself, I think a difficulty with inferencing is an important factor in not understanding other people. If I mis-hear one word in a sentence, I find it really hard to make sense of the sentence. In contrast, although NTs do not always hear every single word, they can usually quite easily work out the overall meaning. The reason for mishearing might be that the environmental noise is too loud, but it could also be when the person uses a slang expression, which I may *know*, but just not use myself in speech. If the word I do not catch is one which I am not expecting, it will not pop up in my head in a list of possible guesses.

One weekend, I was away with some friends and, feeling relatively brave and not content to sit around missing what people were saying all the time, I kept asking for people to repeat themselves, which might have been a bit annoying. On one utterance that I missed, my friend did not repeat, but instead rephrased what he had said. I understood the rephrased version and then after a few more seconds, I worked out what the slang word that he previously used must have been.

When this happens to me, I do not think: "oh, I am experiencing an inferencing problem", but I simply realise I cannot hear/ understand the sentence. So, I find that it can be difficult to distinguish between not physically "hearing" and failing to make inferences. These two difficulties interact intimately with each other.

Good communication tips for spectrum folk

1.   The goal of communication is to understand the other person's point of view.

2.   To do this, it is very important to listen.

3.   Everyone likes talking about themselves. So, if you like talking about yourself/your interests, remember that the other person has equal rights to do the same.

4.   In a conversation, try to ensure that each person can talk about 50% of the time. This helps the conversation to be more equal. No matter how keen you are to talk about yourself or your special interests, remember that the other person will have their own interests and will not want to listen to you talk for 100% of the time.

5.   If you are in a position of leadership, listening is even more important. You might think that a good leader should be dictating to other people what is going to happen and their own point of view. This is part of it. However, you should still not be talking more than 50% of the time.

6.   Remember that your knowledge is different from other people's knowledge. If someone says or does something that is confusing or seems downright nasty, try to work out if they or you are missing a vital piece of information.

7.   It is very important not to jump to conclusions. It is particularly difficult for aspies/auties to understand what the other person is thinking, feeling or implying, so we must be particularly careful.

8.   If you think someone else is being unreasonable, it is a good idea to check what their understanding of the situation is. Asking questions means you can gather lots of facts and make sure you are coming to a sensible and justifiable conclusion. This can also divert you from the dangerous track of jumping to conclusions, making an instant judgement, getting very angry and "losing it" emotionally.

9.   If you are angry that someone has not met your needs, are you sure that you expressed those needs properly in the first place? I once got quite angry that I had not been given something, before I remembered that I had not actually requested it in the first place!

10.   It is very hard to make decisions quickly. In almost any situation, instead of rushing and making the wrong decision, or forming a judgement and getting very angry very quickly, you can always have an escape route. Say: "thanks very much for that information, I am going to think about that very carefully and I will get back to you tomorrow/next week".

11.   This is particularly important if you are becoming emotional/angry. Becoming emotional will cloud your judgement and impede your thinking, so you are unlikely to be able to come to sensible decisions or make sensible interpretations in such a state of mind. Getting angry accesses your primitive "fight or flight" responses and switches off your higher brain power, impeding logic thought, which you actually need. It is much better to think it over once you have cooled off.

12.   If other people's actions/attitudes are still incomprehensible even after some thought, it is a good idea to consult someone else and get their opinion on the situation and/or their recommendation of what you should do. It is smart to recognise when you need extra help and then ask for it.

Communication

One mistake I have seen NT people make is to presume too much knowledge when giving feedback to people on the spectrum. Also, the advice should be positive rather than negative. Only telling someone what *not* to do, does not help them find an alternative behaviour or way of thinking. The above points illustrate the level of detail that you might need to go into, even if the person is very high-functioning. Most NTs do not seem to perceive the need to explain such things in this level of detail, because these things have always been blindingly obvious to themselves.

13.   Reflecting back. When someone tells you something, repeat back to them your understanding of what they said. In this way, any misunderstandings should immediately come to light. I have not yet tried this one out. It seems quite sensible, although I imagine it could get a bit wearing for the other person if I over-do this.

14.   Choose your environment carefully. As I have discovered, I do not get on equally well in every environment, so I need to find understanding people and a way of explaining my differences to them.

15.   Be assertive about your needs. NTs are different to you and will sometimes not be able to anticipate your particular needs and consequently, they may not meet them, causing you stress and bother. Tell people what you need: "slow down", "be literal", "don't expect me to read between the lines", "please put that in writing", or any other need you might have. If you do not ask, you may not get! Practise expressing some of these needs in advance, so you do not have to think on the spot when you are in a tricky situation.

16.   Disclose your aspie/autie status. I sometimes think that I am so skilled at pretending to be normal, that should be sufficient and I should not need anyone to make any allowances for me. However, as much as I often do not want to do this, I am forced to admit

that having to disclose my aspie status to people is sometimes the best way forward. If I say: "I have some areas of difficulty" and I then describe some features of Autism without giving it a name, people may think I am just being particularly fussy. However, if I say "I have a disability, it is called Asperger Syndrome", and then describe the exact same features, I get a totally different response, which is much more caring and helpful.

This makes no sense. To me, label or no label, if someone tells you they need things communicated in a certain way, or that they need specific environmental conditions, you should believe them and try to be helpful. However, from experience, I can tell you this may not happen. As I hope I have explained adequately above, the communication issues are numerous and pervasive, whilst bizarrely apparently my aspie status is pretty much invisible to most people I have ever met in my life. This indicates how much society still needs to learn. I just get hit with people's negative reactions, when they believe that "I can, but I won't", or that I am arrogant, or not listening, or egocentric, or eccentric, or whatever it is that they happen to think.

How to communicate with spectrum folk

When communicating with someone who has more difficulty communicating than I do (this may be a child, a person from a foreign country or a person on the spectrum), I adapt my communication. I use the same method for all of these three different types of people and it seems to work well. Here are some of my adaptions:

1.   My mind is quite simple, and always needs all the relevant details. So, I try to provide others with all the relevant details.

2.   I slow my speech down.

3.   I try to say what I mean.

4.   I think before I start speaking about the simplest way of saying what I want to say. I avoid long words/sentences.

5.   I try to err on the side of providing too much information rather than too little. Personally, being told what I already know once in a while does not usually bother me, and indeed gives me a little breathing space, and I would rather that than be left confused and overwhelmed. However, I am very easily and often confused when a piece of relevant information is missed out and it is assumed that I know it. An example of me erring on the side of providing too much information is when I met a fellow aspie in my local city centre. We were both walking from the train station to the same destination. It was not far, but I had a feeling that this person was not great at finding his way round and that he might get flustered in the crowds of people. Therefore, as we walked and chatted, I provided directions at intermittent intervals, such as "we're going left here"; "now we're turning right". I was not 100% sure that these directions were necessary, but since I was in doubt, I provided the information. The chap I was with did not get offended and I think it made things easier for him. A friend did the same for me when we were on a choir tour in Moscow. He noticed that I never knew how to navigate the underground system, unlike everyone else in our group. He would walk close by me and tell me "left" or "right". I was very grateful for that and it certainly eased my confusion.

6.   I try to be tolerant. One autistic woman I know asks lots of questions but often does not wait for an answer before rushing on to her next question. I try to exercise tolerance and patience. She is almost certainly too busy thinking and processing to be aware of this. Do not think of stuff like this as rudeness, think of it as a lack of conversational skill.

7.   I explain every step and do not leave gaping holes in my sentences for other people to have to infer over the gaps. For example, my friend said to me: "It is difficult going to the park

with both my baby and my dog", and it was not clear to me what she meant. I would have said: "It is difficult going to the park with my baby and the dog because the dog gets quite excited and is difficult to control and because the baby is learning to walk and can now escape from her pram."

8.   When I see that someone does not understand something, I look for a way to break the task/concept down into a list of rules or procedural steps that can be followed with as little interpretation on their part as possible. I think this helps NTs as well as aspies and auties.

The following techniques also really help, but I cannot claim that they are any special adaptions on my part, as this is how I speak anyway:

9.   I do not communicate using complex codes/riddles/ ambiguous ways. Instead, I communicate very literally.

10.   I do not use body language to do part of the work for me.

11.   I do not use slang.

12.   I speak clearly and pronounce every syllable.

This technique is not something I have learned because of (or since) knowing about Autism. For me, these are just obvious adaptions. For example, some years ago (years before knowing I was on the spectrum) I lived with a Japanese girl who, at the beginning, had a very poor ability in English and this was how I communicated with her.

I recently found out that Tony Attwood takes a similar approach. He calls his aspie-communicating style "aspergerese" (Attwood, 2007, p. 224). Some of Tony's adaptions include a careful consideration of what to say and how to say it; avoidance of figures of speech;

allowance of sufficient processing time; avoidance of ambiguity/ subtlety; and not taking offence at too much honesty or lack of eye-contact.

You might be thinking that it must be harder for me to talk with another autistic person who also has a "communication deficit", than with an NT. However, this is often not the case. Many of my miscommunication mishaps simply would not have occurred with an autistic person. Many autistic people explain what they are wanting to say verbally and literally. Therefore, they do not leave you guessing as to what they could possibly be offended about! And they speak directly, not indirectly. If an autistic person was going to tell me that I should not eat an orange, they would say: "you should not eat an orange". With an autistic person, even if you do not *like* what you are being told, at least you *know* what you are being told.

I do not get offended if another aspie/autie I have been socialising with wants to leave and spend some time on their own. I do not get offended if someone does not look in my eyes when we talk. I do not get offended if someone does not acknowledge my presence in passing. I assume they are engaged in their thoughts, as I am in mine, and I do not take it as an offensive slight.

In conversations with other aspies and auties, the communication is usually direct and taking place in one modality: verbally. The conversation is based on the words we are both saying, not upon gestures and what is happening in the background of our environment. For me, this has the effect of the pace being slower and so it is more relaxing. I can then understand everything that is going on and I do not end up exhausted, like a worn-out rag.

Of course, it always helps to have something in common with the person you are communicating with. Aspie/autie conversations will not usually be centred around a hit TV show, the latest fashions, or what the celeb-world is doing. Our conversations are more likely to be fact-based, such as a discussion about the porosity of eggs at different temperatures and the consequences for whether or not to keep them in the fridge! We have similar thinking styles and we probably had similar experiences growing up, so there is that to discuss too. And the best part is exchanging funny stories, because many things that happen to aspies and auties are just hilarious once you realise what has been going on (communication gaffes, being locked up in cupboards by your primary school teacher, answering honestly to questions like: "does my bum look big in this?" and other people's reactions).

Aspies and auties also understand each others' needs. Other spectrum folk believe me when I say that I need quiet to concentrate when I am at work. Of course. However, I have found that it can be harder to convince some NT people of this, because many NTs do not share this particular difficulty themselves. This emphasises my point that "empathy" and "mind-reading" are two entirely different things. In this case, the aspies/auties have empathy with me, but the NTs do not.

What makes a good communicator?

It is taken for granted in much of the Autism literature that NTs are proficient communicators and that spectrum folk are impaired communicators. However, the more I learn, the more I think this is an unfair assessment. I believe that both NTs and autistic people can be potentially good and bad communicators.

A French person talking to an English person will have problems because they are from two different cultures, no matter how good the French person's English is. I think a lot of the "communication deficit" issues actually boil down to cultural ones, which are confused with communication deficits in the minds of many NTs.

Luke Jackson agrees: "It seems to me that non-AS people have their particular way of talking and AS and autistic people have theirs. As usual, because we are in the minority, we are the ones who are misunderstood and ridiculed!" (Jackson, 2002b, p. 100).

I have found that there are at least four types of communicator:

A)   The type of NT who is not particularly intellectual but is very into fashion and appearances. I have difficulty talking with this type of NT because I cannot think what on earth we might have in common. So, thinking of something relevant to say is difficult. I might say "hello", but little else. It is not so much I do not want to talk to them, as I have no idea how to do this.

B)   An intelligent, mind-reading but not empathic NT. This type sees mind-reading as a fundamental human quality and they feel uncomfortable to be around someone who does not have this ability. They cannot quite understand how other people do not have this ability. You might think it surprising that I should have trouble when dealing with such a people-orientated, empathic person. Surely, you are thinking, they have enough empathy for both of us? But they detect that something is odd about me, cannot put their finger on it, but just feel uncomfortable. So, there is a strange awkwardness in the air. Even with the best intentions, neither of us can connect with the other.

C)   An intelligent, mind-reading and empathic NT, who accepts that some people are different, and who is not fazed by this. This type is great, but unfortunately much rarer than types A and B. This type is skilled enough in conversation so that when we talk, it does not stall. They are good at listening and, if I do anything odd, they find it easy to understand and see why. This type is also good at mixing with types A and B, and they have multiple social gears. They can be operating at a very high paced banter with type Bs, they can make small talk with type As and they can do a slower-paced aspie conversation with me. Some of this type may have an autistic parent/relative. Some of my favourite, most kind and helpful NTs are girls with aspie fathers.

D)   An aspie/autie communicator. This type says what they mean, operate at a slower pace, prefer intellectual discussions, and are pretty tolerant of differences/weirdness in others. I have met lots of autistic people, and I find they communicate just fine - they just need to be given the chance to speak. This means having a communication partner who is present, patient, willing to listen to their opinion and non-judgmental. It seems to me that one of the biggest differences is really the "speed" of the conversation. By "speed", I mean how many words per minute are being transmitted/received, but also the complexity of the transmitted information - how far from the purely literal you can go.

I think of communication like a set of gear wheels on a bicycle. Imagine a set of ten gear wheels ranging from very small to large, and arranged in order of size, as on a bike. The gear wheels are numbered from one to ten, one being the smallest gear wheel. The larger gear wheels represent the faster speeds of communication; the smaller gear wheels represent the slower speeds. Every person has their maximum gear size, beyond which they cannot go, because they have reached their maximum processing speed. There is nothing you can do about your maximum gear size. However, in theory, it is possible for everyone to use lower gears, because then you just simply operate slower than your maximum speed. This is the same as sprinting. The one hundred-metre gold medallist is able to run slower than his maximum speed to match the pace of the bronze medallist, but the bronze medallist cannot run faster than his own maximum speed, to catch up with the gold medallist running his best.

To explain my model, I will discuss one hypothetical autie who has a maximum speed of two, a hypothetical aspie who has a maximum speed of four and a hypothetical NT who has a maximum speed of nine. But obviously different people within these groups will have different speeds. Some NTs might only have a maximum speed of three; some aspies might have a maximum speed of eight.

Communication

The medical model of Autism seems to judge proficiency in communication in terms of your personal maximum speed. In my example, the medical model judges our NT (with their maximum speed of nine) to be a good communicator, and our aspie and our autie, with their lower maximum speeds, to be poor communicators.

I propose that this is unfair, because it fails to take account of the fact that communication involves two people and not just one. For a conversation to work, the two parties have to find a compromise speed, which they can both use.

In my model, if our NT is speaking to another NT, both might be using their maximum speed nine, and the communication is fine. If our NT (max speed nine) speaks to our aspie (max speed four), our aspie cannot use any higher gear than four, so it is incumbent on our NT communicator to change down to a lower speed. However, although I said before that in theory, people can use lower speeds, it is my experience that actually using lower speeds is a skill, rather than an innate ability.

In particular, NTs of types A and B often stay at their maximum speed nine, and either do not see a reason to change to a lower speed, or do not have the ability to do so. In this case, the communication does not work, because the speeds are different and the gear wheels "do not mesh".

However, NTs of type C *do* manage to change down to a lower speed when encountering an aspie of speed four. They also select gear wheel four, the wheels mesh, and the communication is fine. Likewise, of course, this does not only apply to NTs. Suppose our aspie (max speed four) is talking with our autie (max speed two). This time, our autie cannot go any faster than speed two, so our aspie has to change down and operate slower and more simply than their usual style. If our aspie fails to do this, does not see the need or does not have the ability, the conversation will not work. If our aspie does this, the conversation will be fine.

Are you eating an orange?

And, naturally, if our NT (max speed nine) is talking with our autie (max speed two), our NT will likewise have to change down even further than for our aspie, to reach gear wheel two. The same principle applies.

According to my model, a "good communicator" is not defined as who has the highest maximum speed. In contrast, a "good communicator" is one who can use their maximum speed *and all other speeds below it, as needed*. No-one should resent having to use a slower speed than their preferred speed, because it must be remembered that if you are the one with the highest maximum speed, the other person cannot come up to meet you and it is therefore your duty to meet them on their speed.

It also follows from my model that aspies do theoretically have an advantage over NTs when it comes to communicating with auties, simply because they are usually operating on a more similar speed in the first place. As you can see from my discussion above regarding how I communicate with people on the spectrum, I highlighted the fact that some of my techniques are not actually adaptions from my normal way of communicating. However, an NT would additionally have to remember and to apply these techniques, which would not be normal for them.

I find it very interesting and amusing to find myself suddenly in a middle position. Usually, my life experience has been such that I am at either end of whatever scale I am on; being average at anything just does not occur. I am much more academically intelligent than most people (I was a straight-A student). On the other side, I am much, much worse at hand-eye co-ordination (learning to juggle took three months of hard work and sheer stubbornness to accomplish what others can learn within one week). These are just two examples, but for almost everything I find myself right at one of the sparsely populated ends of the normal distribution curve. It is like the "class" sketch on TV - it had John Cleese (the tallest, and upper class) and two others (one of middle-height to represent the middle class and a third short man to represent lower class). The three of them talked, explaining that upper-class man looked down on the middle class and lower class, whilst the middle class looked down on the lower class but looked up to the upper class. Whilst they talked, it was funny because the height difference was symbolising the social status. Well, I am almost always the tall one or the short one, never in the middle, but it is only being in the middle that anyone can get a proper perspective on things.

Now, suddenly, in this one area, I find myself in a middle position between some others on the spectrum and NTs and I rather like that. Obviously, I do realise that it is not, objectively, a middle position, on account of the NT population being so large, and the aspie and autie populations so small. So, I am really still at the lower end of the Social Quotient normal distribution curve. However, I am not quite at the very tip of the curve, because there are a few folk who are further towards the tip than me. Learning about, and meeting, other aspies and auties often helps me to see what my issues are. Some people manage brilliantly and they inspire me more than I can say. With some, I see my own issues, magnified. This helps me to understand how NT people might see me and what an enigma I must be to them.

Meeting other people on the spectrum has taught me a lot. I have learned that just because someone may have a slow processing speed, this does not mean that they are any less intelligent than people with a higher processing speed. Even if I have to speak more slowly than usual and in a very literal way, my conversation partner might easily be more intelligent than I am. Also, I believe it is quite possible that some autistic people who are labelled "learning disabled" might, in fact, be very bright. I had previously assumed that being labelled learning disabled or not was 100% due to genetics. However, I now believe that some people on the spectrum may or may not end up with a learning disability label, depending on what happens to them in their lives. For instance, someone on the spectrum who is highly motivated to learn (for example, if they develop a special interest) and with the right circumstances to enable that learning, might progress significantly and not be given a label of learning disability. Another person, with the same severity of Autism but lacking such motivation and being placed in circumstances which hinder their learning, may end up with a learning disability label. Of course, I am *not* at all trying to say here that autistic people with learning disabilities should just try harder. I am also not saying that being labelled as learning disabled is necessarily a bad thing; it might be a very good thing and provide access to much-needed services. There will be some people on the spectrum who would end up with the learning disability label whatever happens and however hard they try, and there will be others who, even if they do not develop a special interest, would never attract a learning disability label. However, I do think there will be some people who could go either way, depending on their personalities and life circumstances.

Also, since Autism involves a developmental *delay*, rather than a developmental *stop*, some people might be labelled learning disabled early on in life, but then go on to develop amazingly later on. It is therefore very important to never write anyone on the spectrum off as unable to learn or progress. Suitable opportunities for learning at all ages should be provided, no matter how many months or years the person may be behind the rest of their age group.

I find the combination of a slow processing speed and a high level of intelligence to be remarkable and unusual, and something I had not come across before I started to learn about Autism. And then, I realise, that is exactly why some people are so confused by me, because I can show them some amazing abilities, but then lack some incredibly commonplace abilities. This bizarre contradiction is one of the things I like best about Autism.

Social Mishap Stories

In my experience, some NTs can be very intolerant of what, to me, are tiny variations from the norm. Many of my problems when something I have said is misunderstood (transmission of communication) boil down to someone else taking offence by implying something I did not mean into what I said.

Many of my communication problems when I am receiving communication can be summed up as "I did not do what they did not literally ask me to do and they then got angry that I did not do it".

Of course, there is a wider background story to this. In most cases, I am not acting in a way that the NT is expecting and they may not understand why. The NT may assume that I am communicating and understanding like an NT and may not realise a communication difficulty exists. They may then, quite naturally, ascribe a negative intent to any of my actions and words that seem inappropriate to them.

I will now give a few additional examples of communication difficulties I have experienced. These examples cover a range of topics and I have highlighted at the beginning the main issue(s) pertaining to each example.

Example 1

Point of difficulty: Literal, direct communication.

In the chapter on communication, I already gave an example ("Are you eating an orange?") of a communication problem when I was the receiver of non-literal information. The following example is the flip-side of this; when I am the communicator but my listener is expecting an indirect communication style:

Are you eating an orange?

The scene: in the office, I am needing to check that a first letter has already been sent, because it says that is has in a subsequent letter I have been asked to sign and I know that I am responsible for accuracy. I have looked in the file, but I cannot see evidence of sending.

Me: "Have you sent this first letter?"

My colleague reacts with anger: "Obviously I sent it, I would not have written that I had sent it in the second letter if I had not; why don't you trust me like the others do? Here is the first letter, it is in the tray..."

In hindsight and with help from other people to understand this situation, I believe that my colleague may have been hearing an implication: "I do not think you have sent this letter and I do not trust you to have done that", although this was not what I was thinking. My thinking: "it is my responsibility to make sure letters that I sign are correct" did not have any bearing whatsoever on my feelings about my colleague's competence as their job. It was merely a reflection of what I considered my responsibilities to be. If it had been anyone else, including any of my bosses, I would have asked whether the letter had been sent in just the same way. I was simply needing information (a yes or no answer) so I asked the question to get it. I do not communicate by hints, so if I had meant what my colleague seemed to have thought I meant, I would have said that.

People may not realise that I do not use implications as much as they do, because they see that I am intelligent and so assume that I have all of the abilities that they have themselves. Because NTs are used to detecting coded messages, they may look for coded messages in what I say, even if none are actually there. They then interpret a message that I am not trying to say and things get horrible. This effect is quite a surprising result of me communicating more simply than other people.

Afterwards, my Autism Counsellor at my local Autism Centre explained to me that it would have been better if I had said:

"Excuse me, so sorry to trouble you, I appear to be muddle-headed today, I know that you have sent this letter, but I am having a little trouble locating it, can you please help me out by showing me where it is?"

It actually took my Autism Counsellor about forty-five minutes of explaining before I could even understand the difference between what I said and this longer NT-style question. I remember having to get out a pad and paper and have my counsellor write down her version, because it was making so little sense to me that I could not remember it and I wanted to learn it for next time. For me, this is a very complicated and convoluted way of saying "have you sent this letter?", and one which I would never have thought of myself in a million years. After a great deal of effort, I now think I understand the difference. Me saying "have you sent this letter?" is a direct question implying that the colleague may not have done something they should have done, whereas the long version implies that the person having the difficulty is me, not them, because I am the one that cannot find the letter.

The second issue in this scenario was that I tend to follow rules exactly to the letter, which is another aspie-thing; we are good rule followers. The rule was that accuracy was the responsibility of the person signing out the letter. However, apparently according to normal social convention, most people would not check every single, last detail of every single letter or other piece of work. Instead, they would check the crucial things and would take other things on trust to save time. This is not me trying to accuse other people of doing things wrong, but it is just what has been explained to me as normal NT behaviour. I was never comfortable doing that, no matter who had prepared the letter and no matter what my opinion of their abilities was. It really was not a personal judgement and I would have (and did) treat work from all of my colleagues including people far senior to me in exactly the same way. For me, it was simple. If I was signing out that the work was correct, I would have to have checked every detail for myself. However, that was another cause of this difficulty. This colleague was expecting me to act like most people would in that situation, but I was not willing to compromise my rule-following tendencies. In my view, other letter-signers were welcome to follow their practices, but I would follow mine.

So, I can now understand my colleague's point of view and why they were offended. I used a direct question to which they took offence and I did that due to my lack of knowledge and skill about how to phrase the question I needed to ask tactfully. On their part, they did not realise about my very simple communication style and took what I said as a personal reflection on their abilities, when no such implication was intended. Their assessment of the perceived slight on their abilities might have been completely right if they had been dealing with an NT. But with me, the situation was different.

Example 2

Point of difficulty: taking the literal words without their context

The scene: In my boss's office.

Me: "I have just discovered that the cleaners are using a cleaning product which includes bleach to clean our mugs. I am very upset about this. Bleach is a very strong chemical. Who can I speak to about this?"

My boss: "The cleaners clean our mugs out of the goodness of their hearts. If you are worried about this choice of cleaning product, you should clean your own mug. If you go to see personnel about this issue, they will be forced to act and the cleaners could get very offended. I recommend that you do not speak to personnel about this."

I thought: "I do not agree with that, cleaners are paid to clean and in any case, the fact that a bleach cleaning product is being used is more important, in my view, than the cleaners potentially being offended. And if I speak to personnel, they will be forced to do something, which is good, because they *should* do something about this situation."

In my colleague's office, I recounted this conversation, just by way of general chat:

Me: "I do not agree with what my boss said, so I am on my way now to speak to personnel about this."

My colleague (in horror): "Do not do that, your boss told you not to!"

Me: "No he did not, he only recommended me not to. So I have the choice!"

My colleague: "No, but he really wanted to tell you not to; he will be really angry if you *do* speak to personnel now."

I continued arguing that surely if my boss had wanted to tell me not to, he would have said that. He is my boss so he is entitled to tell me what to do. I know he is not a shy, retiring person. Why would he *not* tell me something that he wanted to tell me? After some debate along these lines, I decided to trust my friend's instincts over my own and I did not speak to personnel. I was, however, quite stunned that my boss said: "I recommend you do not" when he apparently meant: "You must not". In consequence, I have learned the following rule:

"I recommend" + Authority Figure = "Do not under any circumstances, if you value your life".

119

I now understand that the NT point of view is that adults should not tell one another what to do directly because this is perceived as rude and demeaning to their status as adults. So, they give each other hints with hidden messages when they are wanting to influence each other's behaviour. Fantastic in theory, but this is just not going to work when dealing with me because I am likely to miss the hints.

Example 3

Point of difficulty: Monoprocessing/ body language/context

The scene: Talking with an NT friend. The topic of conversation is my friend's daughter. A woman with obviously bad conversational skills comes up to us and joins in for a bit. This woman leaves.

My friend: "Did you know she is autistic?" (with a head tilt to indicate the departing woman).

Me (not seeing the head tilt, thinking "she" = topic of conversation = her daughter, but surprised because I thought her daughter to be very sociable):

Me: "Really?"

After a bit of quick thinking:

Me: "Uh, did you mean that woman who just left?"

This is an example of me missing the context (my friend's obviously NT daughter and the obviously challenged woman we were speaking with) and the visual clue of the head tilt.

Example 4

Point of difficulty: Mind-reading

Scene: in my boss's office. My boss is working. I am fairly new in my job and have just walked into the office and started talking (well, babbling) about a problem I am having with my work. Hardly having crossed the threshold, I launch straight into the details of the problem.

My boss: "Whoa, your brain is very fast and it is difficult to keep up with you. You have just been trying to solve that particular problem for some time, but I am not familiar with the file or your problem. First, start by telling me the file number of the case you are working on. Then, tell me the nature of the task you are doing. Then, explain what the problem is and remember to take lots of pauses and deep breaths between your sentences."

Because of an inability to read my boss's mind, I assumed that he could understand what I was saying and be immediately up to speed on the problem that I was working on. My boss's reaction to me and his explanation was very constructive and I learned from it. However, this boss did not seem to mind me interrupting his work and always appeared happy to talk to me at any time, so I did not learn from him the knowledge that might have saved me from being the target of a lot of anger, which was the consequence of Example 5, which occurred at a later date, in a different workplace, and in which I acted in exactly the same way...

Example 5

Point of difficulty: Mind-reading

Scene: in my boss's office. My boss is working. I am fairly new in my job and have just walked into the room and started talking (well, babbling) about a problem I am having with my work.

Are you eating an orange?

Hardly having crossed the threshold, I launch straight into the details of the problem.

My boss (angrily): "What?!"

Me (thinking): "Okay, this is my boss, he has to supervise me, but he seems to react badly whenever I ask him questions. Therefore, he must not like supervising me, but unfortunately it is his job to do that, so I have to keep asking him questions. I think he must be grumpy because he does not like doing his job. I wish he would be a bit nicer to me, but I am only doing my job too and I cannot do anything about the fact that he does not like his job."

Some months of this kind of interaction later:

My boss: "When you have some questions about your work, please put your work on this bookshelf over here and I will look at it when I have time and we will discuss it then."

Problem solved.

Because of my inability to read my boss's mind, it did not occur to me that he might be annoyed by me interrupting his work and it certainly never occurred to me to ask him when it would be most convenient for him to talk to me about my work.

With hindsight, I believe my boss may have considered me rude and disrespectful because I had interrupted him whilst he was working. He may have believed the reason for his anger towards me was obvious, because most people would have known not to interrupt someone (particularly a boss) in this way. Perhaps he expected me to get the hint and that was why he did not explain to me how he wanted me to act earlier. However, at the time, the fact that I was approaching him in the wrong way never entered my head, so I did not realise there was anything I could do to stop his angry reaction towards me and I did not alter my behaviour.

Personally, I think I am very good at knowing when someone is angry. Detecting their anger is not the problem. However, I often do not know why they are angry, even if I try to work it out like in the example above, in which I concluded wrongly that my boss just did not like supervising me. If someone does not explain why they are angry, I do not know whether (1) they are just being unreasonable; or (2) there is something I am doing that is upsetting them and which I could change if I knew what it was.

In such circumstances, other people may assume that I know why they are angry and that I am deliberately provoking them. Sometimes, they appear to me to get angrier as time goes on. Perhaps they think that I do not know that they are angry and that if they increase the intensity of the anger, then I will get the message. However, since I *do* know that they are angry, but what I do not know is *why*, this approach is as effective as trying to communicate with a person who only speaks Greek by shouting in English. Or perhaps they become more and more annoyed as time goes on and the pattern repeats itself and that is why the anger appears to increase.

Example 6

Point of difficulty: Mind-reading

After a meeting, my boss told me I had spoken too fast and that the other people at the meeting would have had difficulty understanding all of what I was saying.

I think there are several reasons why I did this:

1.   I am not the most concise person in the world (which you have probably figured out by now!) - sometimes, it takes me a while to explain what I mean. I fear that sometimes when I try to explain myself, other people will lose patience. So, I feel under pressure to explain things quickly to people, before they turn off.

2.   I have had many experiences of not being listened to, which exacerbates the first issue.

3.   I am talking to transmit information, but whilst I am doing this, I am really concentrating on what I have to say and ordering my thoughts. Since I am monochannelled, I do not have any processing ability left to either (1) look at the other people at the meeting; or (2) try to monitor how they are receiving what I am saying. So essentially, when I was talking, I had no idea what the other people were thinking and therefore no idea that I was talking too fast for them.

This boss had previously told me something similar about telephone conversations. He told me when I phone a client, to say my first sentence to introduce the topic of the phone call and then to pause, breathe, let the other person say something and then to continue. This boss had no knowledge of Autism (and neither did I at the time) but he was one of those rare people who knew how to deal with me by instinct.

Faux Pas

A faux pas is when a speaker says something without considering if it is something that the listener might not want to hear or know and which typically has negative consequences that the speaker never intended. Baron-Cohen, O'Riordan, Stone, Jones & Plaisted (1999) conducted a study in recognising faux pas. They found that high-functioning auties and aspies were impaired at detecting faux pas, compared to NT children controls. Furthermore, even when some of the autistic group were able to recognise faux pas, they still produced faux pas themselves.

In my opinion, making faux pas is one of the most painful aspects of being autistic. I am embarrassed to say, this does happen to me with alarming frequency, and it usually leaves me with massive guilt feelings - despite the end of the faux pas definition: "negative consequences that the speaker never intended". For example, once I had a particularly bad day when someone had been pretty angry at me and had lectured me for about twenty minutes for something I considered to be a very good and ethical deed and none of that person's business in any case. I was boiling angry about the situation. Later on that day, I was given a lift home from the pub with two friends. I was having difficulty dealing with the anger that incident had caused and I told my friends all about it, in quite strong terms. I had completely forgotten that one of my friends was distantly related to the person who I was having the problem with. The other friend pointed this out to me and I was completely horrified. Of course I would not have said that if I had remembered - it was an obscure fact lodged somewhere at the back of my mind, which I did not think of at all in that situation. Of course I had not wanted to upset my friend and I felt immensely guilty that I had. I apologised profusely the next day.

This is an example of me actually having all of the necessary information to have avoided the situation (I knew somewhere in the depths of my brain that my friend was a relation of that person's) but I did not manage to access this crucial knowledge at the time. It was like my brain link was missing/too slow/too distant to be useful.

Another time, I told my flatmate that I thought her friend's nose looked like a ski-slope. I had precursed this with the phrase "Can I say something that is not in any way intended to be offensive?" Now, I know this will sound ridiculous and unbelievable to you, but I said that with no malice whatsoever. Her friend's nose was quite unusually curvy, but I did not for one instant think that made her look ugly - it was actually quite a cute snub nose. I thought her nose was interesting and I was just trying to express myself creatively. My flatmate would absolutely not believe that I had not intended a huge insult and she took a massive offence at my comment. I told her over and over again that I did not intend that, but she refused to believe me. She said all kinds of things; how I must have real issues, that I was a nasty person, that I must think that my own body is anatomically perfect and obviously I must have known that her friend was very self-conscious and hated her nose.

I was really upset and kept apologising. That did not work and my flatmate refused to speak to me for a number of weeks. I felt really guilty and questioned myself as to whether what she had said was true. Had I intentionally made a nasty comment? But then I realised that was not right, because I remember the absolute shock when she said that her friend thought her own nose was ugly. I reasoned that as I felt such a big shock being told her nose was less than attractive, that proves I could not have previously thought her nose to be ugly and I could therefore not have been making an intentionally nasty comment about it.

Previously up to that point, I had a rule not to say anything negative about someone's appearance and I was following that rule that day, because in my opinion, her nose shape was not a negative aspect of her appearance. Since that day, I have modified my rule to: "do not say anything neutral or negative about someone's appearance and usually, do not say anything beyond 'you look nice today' ".

These are two examples from my adult life. I cannot remember any examples from my childhood, but there must have been many, because I remember once Mum coming back from band practice and explaining how she had said the wrong thing to one of the other band members. Mum ended her story by saying now she knew what it was like to be me!

A piece of spectacularly unhelpful advice I received once was: "Think before you speak". Thank you very much. Think of what exactly? I am already thinking pretty hard all the time. I have to think hard to process cognitively and intellectually things like Theory of Mind tasks and how to act in social situations, which other people just know how to do instinctively. This is how I try to make sense of a very confusing world and I reckon I am doing a pretty good job in the circumstances.

Conversely, one of my friends has an unusual strategy for coping with faux pas. She is often aware that she can be honest and blunt and will say things that can shock other people. However, whereas I feel embarrassed and guilty about this, she likes being like that and says that the sheer effort of continually monitoring and worrying about everything she could possibly say is so great, that she prefers not to even try. Now, in theory, I would have said that this plan was doomed to failure. However, from talking to her, it seems that her strategy works really well. Through just being herself, other people around her learn that that is just her way and learn not to take offence at anything she says. She also says that her friends appreciate her honesty and can always count on her telling the truth. For example, if some clothes do not suit them and they ask her opinion, she will inform them of this.

I think it helps in these matters that if you are going to say outrageous things, you should make them very outrageous. If you are just a little bit over the line, people are much more likely to believe you are being malicious. However, if you are way out, people are less likely to think this. It sounds to me that my friend's strategy has worked incredibly well and she is now surrounded by people who accept her for who she is. Perhaps I should follow suit.

The Gluten-Free, Casein-Free (GF-CF) Diet

Theory of the GF-CF Diet

This chapter is a discussion of Autism as a metabolic condition and the Gluten-Free, Casein-Free (GF-CF) diet as an intervention. Gluten is a substance found in some grains and casein is in milk. The GF-CF diet is one in which gluten, casein (and a few other foodstuffs) are avoided, as will be explained in detail below.

Gastrointestinal symptoms relating to Autism feature prominently in anecdotal accounts, but are largely ignored by the scientific community.

In one study, clinically significant gastrointestinal symptoms occurred in 46% of three hundred and eighty-five children on the autistic spectrum, compared with only 10% of ninety-seven controls (Melmed, 2000, cited in Wakefield et al., 2002). This indicates that a person on the autistic spectrum is much more likely to have gut problems than a random member of the population. So, why should this be? One theory is that Autism is the consequence of a metabolic disorder. The gut-brain connection is well recognised in medicine, which means the intestine and the brain can have a parallel involvement in the same disease process (Quigley & Hurley, 2000). Essentially, if something is wrong with the brain, there is likely to be something wrong with the gut, and vice versa.

Shattock et al (1991) and Sun et al (1999), both cited in Wakefield et al. (2002) proposed that Autism may be caused by inappropriate central activity of dietary-derived opioid peptides from the gut. The theory is that gluten and casein are not being completely broken down in the guts of autistic people, resulting in the generation of opioid peptides, which would not be generated by NTs.

Increased intestinal permeability in children with Autism has been reported by Horwath et al (2000) also cited in Wakefield et al. (2002). This means that too much matter is able to pass into the body through the gut wall; the gut is therefore a "leaky gut". This increased intestinal permeability may mean these opioid peptides are absorbed into the body, instead of being digested. It is already known that opioids from prenatal drug abuse can permanently disturb the developing brain, causing learning difficulties and problems with interpersonal relationships (Zagon, 1985, cited in Wakefield et al. 2002). Hence, it is postulated that exposure to opioid excess during early cerebral development may adversely influence the brain (Wakefield et al., 2002).

Fantastic, so if this theory is correct, I now I learn that I am similar to the result of a drug-addicted mother - but instead of the drug originating from a needle, the drug is my case is actually being created during digestion of gluten and casein. There are some things I really do not enjoy learning. However, my being in denial and ignorance of this would not have helped, so I decided to try the diet and see for myself.

The "leaky gut" theory also provides a possible explanation for the immune system working better on a GF-CF diet. According to this theory, one effect of autistic people eating gluten and casein is that, since it is not normal for large opioid peptides to leak out through the gut wall into the body, the immune system will leap on these apparent "intruders", setting off an immune reaction. The immune system can be kept so busy attacking the foods that we eat, that it does not have much energy to deal with actual illnesses. Hence, by excluding the source of the opioid peptides, the immune system is no longer under the constant pressure of attacking these peptides and can do its normal job much more efficiently.

Although I have looked at some of the research in support of the GF-CF diet, I should say that I am not a medical professional and I am not qualified to comment as to whether this theory, purely as a theory, is correct or not. However, what I can tell you is that I have considerable experience of following this diet, as will be explained further on in this chapter. As a consequence of these experiences, I support this diet entirely. From personal experience, I am convinced that there is something going wrong in my gut which is causing severe pain and digestive problems when I eat gluten and casein, and from my broader learning, I am equally convinced that gluten and casein are also disturbing our brain functioning. So, I feel very confident that the gut and brain are being impacted upon by gluten and casein, in at least some people on the Autistic Spectrum. However, exactly how this disturbance comes about, I am not qualified to say. I also cannot say for certain whether everyone on the spectrum is affected.

Rules of the GF-CF diet

Luke Jackson (2002a) says that by removing certain offending foods, the production of the opioid peptides stops. Jackson advocates a Gluten-Free, Casein-Free (GF-CF) Diet in which the following foods must be avoided:

> Casein, lactose, milk, whey, gluten, barley, malt, oats, rye, spelt, wheat, monosodium glutamate, aspartame, E621 and yeast extract.

According to Luke, eating gluten and casein causes black rings around the eyes, stomach aches, and diarrhoea, all of which I have experienced. Luke's brother, Ben Jackson (an autie), after starting the GF-CF diet, became more fully aware of his surroundings, and no longer "away in his own little planet Autism" (Jackson, 2004, p. 68).

Although it may seem quite simple to avoid these foods, there are a few complications.

After starting the diet, I became very sensitive to even very small quantities of these offending foods. As a general rule, most processed food such as ready-meals, soups, sauces, packet soups, pot noodles, will include at least one of these ingredients. Consequently, my shopping basket tends to be full of fruit, vegetables, meat, rice and soya milk and I prepare most of my meals from scratch. This is probably a good thing, because it makes it very difficult to be unhealthy if you are strictly following this diet - most unhealthy foods are excluded.

Restaurants are a major problem, because even if you choose something that does not inherently contain gluten, there is a large possibility of cross-contamination in the kitchens. For instance, I have often felt ill after eating chips, because they have been cooked in the same fat as something containing wheat. I now only rarely eat out, because I do not want to be ill.

I have to read the ingredients list of everything that I buy. This is time-consuming at first, but I have gradually learned what products are okay and if I keep buying these, there is not usually a problem. However, sometimes manufacturers do change the ingredients (all of a sudden, the brand of crisps I was buying started to contain wheat) so it is best to re-check now and again.

Beware: it is not compulsory for small traces of foods to be stated in the ingredients lists! However, small traces are sufficient to make some of us ill.

Remember this all applies to medications as well as foods! Many medications include wheat, milk and/or aspartame. Aspartame is a sweetener and is added to products such as soluble remedies for colds and flus and soluble fibre drinks, as I discovered to my cost. I found that the symptoms of having a cold are much more bearable than the symptoms of taking such a cold remedy!

My Experiences of the GF-CF diet

I discovered Luke Jackson's "User Guide to the GF-CF diet" (Jackson, 2002a) early on in my Autism journey, whilst still on the waiting list for a diagnosis. So, learning of this, I decided to try removing just wheat, initially, from my diet. As far as I was aware, I did not have any stomach problems and my hypothesis was that the diet would not make any difference. I also really hoped that there was no difference because avoiding eating wheat seemed practically impossible. I gave my "no wheat" diet a one week trial, simply substituting GF bread and GF pasta for my usual choices in the supermarket. During that week, I was surprised how good I felt and I realised for the first time in my life what it was like to have no pains in my stomach whatsoever. Before that, I had had continual, frequent but minor stomach pains that I had taken to be just "what stomachs felt like" because it was normal for me. At the end of that week, I tried eating wheat again. At first, I was hopeful - there seemed to be no effect and I was very relieved at the thought that whatever was wrong with my stomach, it was not gluten-related. I really love crumpets and pitta bread! However, fifteen minutes later, I had a massive stomach ache. I repeated the same experiment the following week, with the same results. From that point onwards, I removed wheat, malt, maltodextrin, rye, barley, aspartame and monosodium glutamate from my diet. I was essentially gluten-free, except at that stage, I was still eating oats (which contain gluten), because I could not notice any adverse effects from oats. Also, at that time, I did not try giving up casein. I had not noticed any bad effects from milk and I was concerned that, as a vegetarian, milk was too vital a source of protein and calcium for me to safely give up.

I spent the following year perfecting supermarket shopping according to this diet; this was difficult. Almost everything that is not raw fruit and vegetables in the supermarket (for example, tinned soup, most types of crisps, pesto, cooking sauces, soy sauce, salad cream, veggie burgers) seemed to contain wheat, monosodium glutamate, malt, maltodextrin, malt extract or yeast extract. However, I got quite good at this and it became rare that I felt ill through any meal that I prepared myself.

Are you eating an orange?

It was all going swimmingly until two years ago. Something was making me feel ill although, unusually, I could not figure out what it was. I mentioned this to my colleague, who pointed to the cappuccino I had in my hands at the time and pointed out how many artificial additives there could be in that drink. Good point, I thought, perhaps that is it. So, I swapped my daily cappuccino the following day for a mug of warm milk and did the same the next day. Disastrous! Although I had not experienced problems with milk before, this sudden increase in my usual quantity of milk seemed to have tripped a switch and I was really ill. I desperately did not want to cut out milk from my diet (as I said before, I was vegetarian) and so I tried to cut down the amount of milk/cheese that I was eating instead of stopping it altogether. No use. As the week continued, I had diarrhoea which I could not make stop and I got more and more exhausted through not being able to digest food properly. By the end of the week, I was a crying, sorry mess. I was going to bed with stomach spasms - like there was an alien leaping about in my gut and I even woke up in the middle of the night with the pain. So, I decided time had come for drastic action and I cut the milk out of my diet completely. Within thirty-six hours, the stomach pains and spasms had stopped. Whew, I thought. So, I replaced my usual milk with rice milk, bought a dairy-free sunflower margarine, cut out cheese, and replaced my bio yoghurts with soya bio yoghurts. For additional protein, I bought packs of soya mince, which I froze. Great, I thought, this is not so hard. However, I was wrong.

My initial feeling-better was short lived; my diarrhoea came back and I could not shift it. I investigated the possibility of a Candida infection and started the candida diet (no caffeine, alcohol or vinegar and hardly any fruit to minimize sugar). I cut out oats, and I began eating meat. At some point, I found out from Marilyn le Breton that the brand of rice milk I had chosen was a big mistake as it contained barley and malt (in a proportion small enough not to be required to be listed in the ingredients, but large enough to make me ill). So, to my shock and dismay, I had in fact been eating gluten again for the previous two or three months, due to my attempts to eliminate casein! Still feeling ill, I tried cutting down my diet to a bare minimum of things then re-introducing foods back into my diet more slowly. I even tried various digestive enzymes and many different types of supplements. Many variations and numerous kitchen-reshuffles later, I was still ill and feeling pretty desperate about it. After trying just about every possible diet permutation, my doctor proposed that it might be irritable bowel syndrome due to stress. I was so ill by this point that I decided to test the theory and got signed off work due to illness for a few weeks. That worked marvellously. In the course of being this ill, I had lost fourteen percent of my bodyweight. However, after two weeks of sick leave, I had put seven percent straight back on again. I realised then that I absolutely had to lower my general stress level, and I proceeded to reorganise my life accordingly.

Now, to my amazement, gratitude and relief, my stomach is now much better. It is amazing! I have noticed large changes in my general health since being on the GF-CF diet. Unless I have infringed my diet, I no longer get the painful stomach aches. I have also managed to put on weight, no longer being too skinny. I have still got some irritable bowel symptoms, which I control using various methods such as Tai Chi, meditation, the Alexander Technique and (please do not laugh) social stories that I make up and tell myself. Since these remaining symptoms vanish completely at certain times, e.g. on holiday, I know these are stress-related and not food-related.

Nowadays, when I do accidentally infringe the GF-CF diet, I have much more severe pains than before starting the diet. Luke Jackson says that he and his brothers also react worse to "bad foods" compared to when they first started their GF-CF diet (Jackson, 2002a).

As well as not having the intestinal problems, my immune system functions much better on the GF-CF diet. I hardly ever catch colds now, in contrast to pre-diet, when I seemed to catch every single cold going around; also, most of my childhood was spent with a runny nose. I have one particular memory of my ballet teacher complaining because I was sniffing every three seconds. What did she want, snot all over the floor? An improved immunity to colds is also described by Lauren Goldman Marshall, whose autistic child no longer has a constant runny nose after starting a GF-CF diet (Ariel & Naseef, 2006).

Although as far as I am aware, this is not the case with me, I understand that some people's communication can be highly affected by whether or not gluten is included in their diet. In my case, eating gluten does not appear to have any effect on my communication that I can notice. Eating gluten has never prevented me talking or interacting. Now, I just enjoy the lack of stomach aches, diarrhoea and frequent colds.

When I make mistakes with my diet (which I have done quite often), I certainly do suffer, but I can still go to work and function. I tend to feel ill for one or two days. However, I understand that some people who eat gluten by mistake may feel ill for a few weeks. I have a fledgling theory that the severity of someone's Autism may be directly related to the severity of the effect of eating gluten and casein that the person experiences. In someone with severe Autism, I believe that gluten and casein messes up the pathways between their senses and their brain; hence, communication and sensory systems are very much affected. In someone with less severe Autism, I believe that the brain manages to cope more normally, although the gut system is still very much affected. I met Donna Williams (an autie) at a conference and she said that gluten messes up her senses. She assumed the same for me, which was not the case. Eating gluten makes me feel generally "ill all over" and suffer diarrhoea and an impaired immune system, but my senses still work as normal, as far as I am aware. Perhaps the people with the smallest attention tunnels may have their communication affected by gluten because the gluten might have the effect of constricting their already extremely narrow attention tunnels still further. The focus of this narrowed tunnel may be further drawn away from communication due to stomach pains or general body pains.

So, my conclusion is that the GF-CF Diet is necessary for me (and the whole diet, not just a bit of it). I have also concluded that a lot of my additional difficulties are probably due to irritable bowel syndrome due to stress, instead of being a direct result of some food intolerances. I hope you can see from my sorry and confused story, just how complicated dietary intervention can be, and I would advise anyone trying it to get help rather than go it alone. These things really need a holistic approach, because in my case, looking at diet change alone, without changing the stress in my life, did not work. Your entire life needs to be right for you (right foods and low stress levels), in order to feel truly well.

Before starting the GF-CF diet...

I think this diet is very important for many, and maybe all people on the spectrum, but it is not for the faint-hearted. I do not know if everyone on the spectrum is affected by gluten and casein. I have heard that the autistic spectrum is actually a bunch of different conditions which just happen to share the Triad of Impairments. Therefore, it is possible that some people's type of Autism may be affected by diet and other people's not. There are many autistic people I know who have refused to try the diet or who are not able to try the diet. However, I do not know anyone who has tried the diet but has not found an improvement in their health. I have made many mistakes with it and can recommend the following:

(1) Before starting the diet, get in touch with Paul Shattock at the University of Sunderland and get your urine tested for peptides. This will give you a clue as to whether you are on the right track by going GF-CF; your GP and gastroenterologist are unlikely to be able to offer you any useful tests. After you are already GF-CF, the test may not work, so do this now.

Are you eating an orange?

(2) Also before starting, get your doctor to test for celiac disease. Again, once you have eliminated gluten from your body, this test will not work. It is quite probable that the test will be negative because our gluten intolerance is usually different to celiac disease, but if this test does turn out to be positive, you may be entitled to gluten-free food on prescription. However, do not, whatever you do, make the mistake of thinking that a negative result for celiac disease proves that you do not need this diet.

(3) I am not sure if you can do the diet by halves, e.g. cutting out the gluten but not the casein or vice versa. I found that I had to cut out both, ultimately, but I cannot say whether this is true for everyone.

(4) It is preferable if you can get some support with this diet. I consider myself quite an intelligent person, but I got into quite a pickle with it. I used a web forum run by Marilyn le Breton and Rosemary Kessick, who are now contactable at the following website: www.respectrum.co.uk. The other sources of help I used were the books listed under Recommended Reading at the back of this book.

(5) If you are a vegetarian/vegan, you might want to rethink that. I was a vegetarian from age eleven to thirty (when I started strictly following all rules of the GF-CF diet). I stopped because I was concerned that excluding both milk and meat would be very unhealthy. I reconciled this with my conscience by saying to myself that, whilst I would like to continue being a vegetarian out of concern for the animals, it was just not possible to do this and remain healthy.

(6) Buy "the AiA Gluten & Dairy Free Cookbook" compiled by Marilyn le Breton (Le Breton, 2002). There are tons of good ideas for all sorts of breads, cakes, sweets, main courses and much more. This will be your cooking bible.

Please remember that none of the information contained in this book is designed to be taken as medical advice. Always consult a qualified medical practitioner before implementing any dietary intervention.

Food substitutions

At first, the idea of following this diet terrified me. Wheat and milk are such common parts of our western diet, it seemed impossible to live without one, let alone both. However, I am here to tell you that it is perfectly possible and very nice meals are definitely achievable. In fact, there are many specialised products available, so you and/or your loved one are most certainly not going to starve. Here is a list of some of the food substitutions I use:

Are you eating an orange?

I do not buy	I do buy
Normal bread	Gluten-Free bread from the "Free From" section of my local supermarket, or I make my own bread using a recipe from "The AiA Gluten & Dairy Free Cookbook" (Le Breton, 2002).
Normal pasta	Gluten-Free pasta from the "Free From" section of my local supermarket.
Cows' Milk	Soya Milk or Rice Milk (check carefully to ensure no offending ingredients). I am not sure if this is against the strict rules, but I also appear to be doing well with Goats' milk. (All from supermarkets.)
Breakfast cereal/ porridge oats	Buckwheat flakes, Millet flakes, Quinoa flakes (from health food shops or bought online), used in substitution for porridge oats, or have a nice fry up of bacon, eggs, tomatoes, mushrooms, potatoes.
Normal yoghurt	Soya yoghurt (supermarkets).
Normal butter/ margarine	Dairy-Free margarine (supermarkets).
Normal cheese	Dairy-Free cheese or Goats' cheese (as above, I am not sure if this is within the strict rules). (Supermarkets.)
Normal sausages (which contain wheat)	Gluten-Free sausages, or I stick to pure meats such as chicken, lamb, beef and pork. (Supermarkets, butchers' or farm shops.)

See? This diet is perfectly possible.

The GF-CF Diet

I am a huge fan of this diet and support it wholeheartedly. However, this diet can be very powerful and is not to be messed with! Undertaking this diet should be done with the utmost seriousness, commitment and support.

There are two reasons for this:

1.   The diet is difficult (since wheat and milk are very common western foods) and getting it wrong is painful. Whilst I ate wheat all the time, my body had a level of tolerance to it and I had continual but small stomach pains. Now, if I accidentally eat wheat, the tolerance is no longer there and I will be in serious pain. Everyone responsible for the person doing the diet must ensure the diet is adhered to at all times. One person sabotaging the diet because they do not believe in it will cause a lot of pain. It may be better not to do the diet at all then to have someone going on and off gluten repeatedly.

2.   This diet might significantly improve someone's developmental level! Whilst this may not sound like a problem, it can bring up some difficulties that did not exist before. For example, a change in brain chemistry could make an adult want to have friends for the first time, but since this is completely new, the skills to do this will most likely not be there. Additional learning, such as appropriate personal space boundaries, will have to take place. The person may need support if the diet gives them a huge developmental leap such as this. This is not such an important concern for children – improving their developmental level will have big advantages for them and they are developing relatively quickly at any rate. However, what about for an adult receiving part-time support by social services who are not expecting such a development?

One big change can be for a person who was previously very under-sensitive to their circumstances and the effect they are having on the world, suddenly changing and becoming much more self-aware and sensitive. I personally think this is a good thing, but it is not easy to make this transition.

When you start the diet, you become very sensitive to even very small quantities of the offending foods. Trying to limit your consumption instead of totally cutting them out, in my experience, does not work. In fact, this may be worse than not doing the diet at all, since you may get high and go through withdrawal symptoms each time this happens.

Even if the diet helps, different people find it helps by different amounts. Some people might find that it helps them a bit, but then decide they would prefer to continue to eat gluten and casein. This is not my choice, because I believe that gluten and casein are damaging. However, everyone is entitled to their own choice.

By mentioning these things, I am not at all trying to put you off this diet, which I think is a great thing and really important. I just want to give as much information of the advantages and disadvantages as possible, so you can make an informed decision for yourself.

Why the GF-CF Diet is not yet mainstream

It mystifies me why this diet, which could have amazing overall consequences for the health of people on the spectrum, is not currently recommended by the mainstream medical profession. I happened across this diet during my own research, because I was interested in reading personal accounts written by others on the spectrum. My GP, my local Autism Centre and the National Autistic Society did not mention, suggest or recommend this diet. And yet, I believe it is so fundamental. Why is this?

Knivsberg, Reichelt, Hoien & Nodland (2003) put ten autistic children on a GF-CF diet for one year and compared their progress with ten autistic children not on a GF-CF diet (controls). In the diet group, resistance to communication, social isolation and strange behaviours decreased, whilst willingness and ability to communicate increased. Hence, there was a significant reduction in autistic behaviours. In the control group, autistic behaviours had worsened in 50% of the group and improved in the other 50%.

Millward, Ferriter, Calver, & Connell-Jones (2004) (also known as the Cochrane Review) looked at all relevant randomised control trials involving diets including the elimination of gluten, casein, or both, and found that the Knivsberg et al. (2003) study was the only study that fitted their inclusion criteria. Millward et al. (2004) concluded that the Knivsberg study lent support to the anecdotal reports of the benefits of a GF-CF diet, but felt unable to recommend it based on this single study.

Basically, even if sixty million autistic people tried the diet and all of them wrote books supporting the diet, this would be completely discounted as not being double-blind, relevant randomised control trials fitting the proper inclusion criteria. So sixty million books would, in the eyes of the medical profession and the scientific community, count as no evidence whatsoever. The effect of this is you have to be very strong, you have to go against the advice of your doctor and you have no support from the state (there is no financial support for the increased cost of food). The effect on people who are not so keen to experiment as myself, is they feel put-off from trying the diet because it does not come with a medical recommendation. They, or their children, continue to feel ill, perhaps throughout their whole life. This is tragic!

Referring to Millward et al. (2004), the Scottish Intercollegiate Guidelines Network (2007) "SIGN Guideline" in relation to ASD says: "there is insufficient evidence on the use of casein and gluten exclusion diets for children and young people with ASD and therefore no recommendation can be made" and "Gastrointestinal symptoms in children and young people with ASD should be managed in the same way as in children and young people without ASD" (Scottish Intercollegiate Guidelines Network, 2007, p. 19).

The "insufficient evidence" point might be reasonable, if by insufficient evidence you only include the scientifically conducted "relevant randomised control" trials on which the Millward team were focussing. However, the second quotation, and the lack of any positive statement in support of the GF-CF diet, makes me angry. One of my friends was very sick as a child and had regular vomiting spells which varied in intensity - he ended up on drips in hospitals about four different times and no-one could figure out why. He would then be sent home when he was no longer so dangerously skinny and the whole thing would start again. He was indeed "treated as a child without ASD" (no-one has diagnosed him), which meant that specialist after specialist could find nothing wrong with him. This went on for years, during which at its worst point, he lost a year's growth in height through being so sick. Eventually, his parents realised the sickness was something to do with him drinking cows' milk. They stopped him drinking milk and he got much better. I understand that some people do recognise their own intolerances to gluten and/or casein. However, other people may feel strongly attracted to eating only (or a lot of) foods containing these things. Personally, I love gluten!

I visited a gastroenterologist during my search for the truth, who ignored my Autism/GF-CF diet theory, told me he thought it was not that which was making me ill, wrote "self-diagnosed autistic" on my records after I asked him not to, and arranged a whole battery of tests for other conditions, two of which involved me ingesting nuclear substances, simply because he did not know what was wrong with me. I refused these tests, not wishing to be irradiated when I already knew that if I avoid gluten and casein, I am not ill. I was also offered anti-depressants, not because I was depressed, but to suppress all the nerve endings to my gut so I could therefore eat what I liked with no problems. That seemed like a really stupid solution to me - diarrhoea was telling me that something inside was going badly wrong, so to mask the symptoms would not cure anything and yet this was a choice I was being offered in full seriousness. I found the whole experience with this gastroenterologist pointless and very stressful. I do wonder what it must be like for people who are more trusting of doctors than myself, for those less able to stand up for themselves and their rights and to choose a commonsense course of treatment for themselves.

The SIGN Guideline is what GPs and other Autism/health professionals in Scotland will base their recommendations on. So, this is why, if you go to your GP as an autistic person and complain of bowel troubles, the GF-CF diet is not recommended to you. I meet many autistic people now in various parts of my life, who I think could be helped by this diet if only they knew about it (and in some cases, if they were supported to follow it).

I feel very disappointed in the SIGN Guideline, because it ignores all the anecdotal evidence and ignores all of the other studies which did not fit into their criteria. For example, Whiteley, Rodgers, Savery & Shattock (1999) conducted a gluten-free trial with twenty-two autistic children for five months. When they asked the parents to rate its effectiveness on the child's behaviour, 67% said they thought the diet had led to clear or substantial improvements in their child's autistic behaviours. Also, 60% of parents involved with gluten challenge (when gluten is reintroduced after having been cut out) associated this with worsening of autistic behaviours. However, I feel the most important testimony was that 94% of parents confirmed their child would continue with the GF diet after the study. Trust me, going gluten-free is so difficult in the will-power sense (with all the nice foods you want to eat but cannot), difficult in the academic sense (because of all the hidden ways people find to sneak one of the forbidden substances into innocent-seeming foods; you can try your best to follow the diet but still end up eating gluten accidentally), highly antisocial (when your friends have to go to *your* choice of pub because it is the only one which does baked potatoes) and really expensive (gluten-free bread from the supermarket cost me £4.20 per week before I started baking my own, whereas wheat-based bread could be bought for 40p), that the parents must have found the effects really, really, really awesome, to wish to continue with this. Does the 94% approval rating from parents - despite all of the above issues - mean nothing to the scientific community?

Ignoring the wealth of anecdotal evidence and the studies that do not meet *all* the criteria is, in my opinion, going to lead many people away from the right path to better health. Although we are proceeding in the scientifically correct "cautious manner", I am afraid that we are going in the wrong direction. Whilst I personally do not suffer too badly from gluten, in my opinion, this will directly hinder more people from being able to communicate and more people will spend too much of their childhood throwing up instead of growing up. (Perhaps I will start a GF-CF crusade; my slogan could be: "Grow up, don't throw up"! But I suppose that could be confused with an anti-drinking campaign though...). But seriously, the SIGN Guideline could have mentioned, just one sentence, that some people have found it helpful. In my opinion, the public have a right to know this.

Also, the conclusion that "gastrointestinal symptoms in children and young people with ASD should be managed in the same way as in children and young people without ASD" seems a bit of a leap from the starting point of "no conclusive proof available". In my opinion, the lack of conclusive proof comes simply from the fact that not enough studies have been done. Perhaps there should also be a contradictory statement saying that neither is there any conclusive negation of proof available. I am sorry that this is the best official advice the Autism field can offer people on this subject.

Some people think that these dietary effects, with toxins originating from food damaging the brain, might be the cause of Autism in the first place. I would not be surprised if this turns out to be close to the truth.

Facial Recognition and Facial Distortions

Not recognising people's facial expressions and/or seeing severe distortions in facial features are, for some autistic people, some of their most major difficulties. These are generally under-recognised problems. However, these issues can now be treated and should be addressed as early as possible in life (see next chapter).

A growing body of literature suggests that autistic people have difficulty with the recognition of faces and facial expressions. Obviously, the ability to recognise other people's faces is very helpful for successful interpersonal relationships and for life in general.

O'Conner, Hamm, & Kirk (2007) conducted a study using EEG technology to measure event-related potentials (ERPs) and found that aspie adults took longer to process faces and facial regions than NTs. This was evidenced by delayed N170 latencies, which is a negative deflection that is largest in amplitude over posterior-temporal electrodes and is particularly sensitive to faces.

Schultz et al. (2000) used functional magnetic resonance imaging to study face and object perception in high-functioning auties and aspies relative to NT controls and found the autistic group demonstrated a pattern of brain activity during face discrimination that is more typical of non-face, object discrimination. In other words, the region of the brain in NTs which is specialised in processing faces does not seem to work in autistic individuals, who instead have to use the part of the brain which processes objects in general. This means that faces are processed as if they were objects. Face perception is normally a holistic process, relying on the spatial configuration of facial features, whereas object recognition relies on the detection of individual features (Schultz et al., 2000). Therefore, autistic people tend to be slower and/or less able than NTs to process faces holistically and/or according to the spatial relationships between features (O'Conner et al., 2007).

Are you eating an orange?

There may be at least three different reasons why recognition of faces is difficult:

1.   Some people have prosopagnosia (also known as face blindness), which is a disorder of face perception where the ability to recognise faces is impaired. Some people who have prosopagnosia cannot process a whole face simultaneously, without distortions. If they look at the nose, they cannot process the eyes; if they look at the eyes, they lose the mouth. Faces can look like a confusing, moving, shifting set of parts. The mouth may move up to the forehead. Features may blur, swirl or disappear. This is not my personal experience, but is the experience of some auties and aspies. If you cannot see a whole integrated face in the first place, it is very unlikely that you are going to be able to recognise that person again unless they happen to be wearing the same clothes.

2.   Although I do not see facial expressions as distorted and although I can see a whole face simultaneously, I do have a lot of difficulty in recognising people (sometimes, even people I know really well), so I reckon that I do have prosopagnosia and that I am probably processing faces as if they were objects. This does work to some degree, because a face is a type of object. However, lacking the specialised face-processing area, my ability to recognise faces is not as good or accurate as NTs' recognition of faces.

3.   Because I am generally being bombarded with more information than I can process (due to gestalt perception), in a social interaction, I am devoting my attention to thinking and to listening, and very little attention is therefore left for visual processing and for making an effort to remember the person's face. So, it may be that I cannot remember the face of someone who I have only met a few times, because I have not been able to devote enough processing power to carefully observing and then remembering their face.

Another common problem is metamorphosis. This is where:

"Faces (or parts of faces) will often become geometric shapes, colours may change and in extreme cases the face (or part of the face) may appear to become that of a face of a different animal e.g. a spider or a hamster. In rare cases the face may become monster-like. The size of the face or parts of the face may become grossly distorted. Sometimes the face becomes twisted, elongated and vibrates. Rarely it appears to turn upside down. Metamorphosis can be extremely disturbing and upsetting for a child." (Jordan, 2009).

Another significant problem can be timing. Perhaps due to monoprocessing, there may be de-synchronisation of speech sounds with the movement of the mouth. This can affect auditory processing abilities. An in-depth analysis of the many face-related problems for those on the spectrum is beyond the scope of this work, but detailed information can be obtained from Ian and Beatrice Jordan (see next chapter and the Recommended Reading and References at the back of this book).

In my personal experience, I can recognise people who I know well, but not people who I may have only met once or twice, or people I only meet very infrequently. This can be very embarrassing when there is someone who clearly knows who I am, but who I do not recognise at all. This often inhibits me from starting a conversation with them. At church, one lady had been friendly to me once, some months ago, but when she approached me more recently, I could not recognise her. She realised that I did not know who she was, asked me about it and she obviously felt hurt when I admitted I did not know who she was. I did remember that someone had been kind to me some weeks previously, so in that way I did actually remember her. I just could not remember her face. She probably thought that I was selfish and that her kind acts had gone unrewarded because I had not appreciated it enough to even bother to remember who she was. Not recognising your communication partner makes me and other aspies/auties feel very unsure and "on the back foot" about approaching someone in the first place. Also, if the other person realises that you do not recognise them, this can cause them to feel hurt and offended, which starts the interaction off badly.

In the workplace, I have had problems when I failed to recognise my clients. Usually, given the context, I could work it out, but once I had a difficulty when I met one client in the corridor of a building where many other companies also had their offices. Thankfully in that instance, they spoke to me first and I worked out who they were. But the added difficulty and insecurity this causes does make it quite hard to approach people sometimes and this should not be underestimated.

Another example regarding face-blindness happened when I was giving training to three colleagues at work. I knew two of these colleagues well, but I had only met the third once before. I did not recognise the third colleague when I started the training, but knowing that I am bad with faces, I was not too surprised about that. I worked out who he was from knowing the names of the three people who were supposed to be there and from recognising the other two. We all sat together in one room for three hours for the duration of the training. Directly after the training, I went on a hunt around the office to look for some study materials for them. After finding the study materials, I went to find my colleagues. They had left the training room and I *still* could not recognise the third colleague, despite having just spent the last three hours sitting one metre away from him. Again, I had to work out who he was from the context of the situation. Bloomin' ridiculous!

The other day, I met two new people. Being aware of how difficult I find it to recognise people and my natural inability to process and remember faces very well, I tried to fixate on a very obvious feature of their appearances to help me remember. Unfortunately, both men had dark brown, bushy curly hair and beards. I do remember thinking one looked slightly more like a teddy bear than the other. I deduce from the fact I am trying to remember them by one or two obvious features, that I am doing this because I am not actually able to process or store an image of them in my head. I am a bit concerned that if I met them again, I would not be able to distinguish which one was which. If I met either of them out of context (such as in the supermarket or another place where I did not expect to see them), I would probably not recognise them at all.

Glasses with Coloured Lenses

One of my most remarkable and startling findings has been experiencing the effects of glasses with coloured lenses. The lenses are tinted a particular colour which bests suits the individual. No-one knows exactly why they work. But they are brilliant! My understanding is that most people on the spectrum would benefit from using such glasses, and also many people who are not on the spectrum; in particular, those who are dyslexic and/or dyspraxic. I cannot over-emphasise the importance of this intervention because, contrary to popular belief, it is simply not necessary to live with an inefficient sensory system.

A balanced sensory system = calm.

I discovered these glasses almost by accident; none of the Autism-related organisations I am involved with had previously mentioned this to me. However, if you want to sort out your sensory processing issues, this is definitely the way to go. As I am finding, the best advice often comes from other people on the spectrum or parents, and it is from one such parent that I learned about this magical intervention.

After having seen a documentary about the Jackson family (two children of which got glasses with coloured lenses), I was dubious about whether such glasses would be any use to me, for two reasons. Firstly, compared to the Jackson children and some of my friends, I concluded that any sensory issues I might have would be pretty mild. For example, unlike Luke Jackson, I do not have any problems with walking in a straight line down a corridor. So, I was not sure that coloured lenses would have any effect on me. Secondly, I had assumed that to see this kind of specialist would involve a trip to London, a long waiting list and fees of hundreds of pounds, all to check out something that I was not sure would make any difference to my life. I was wrong on both points.

Glasses with Coloured Lenses

Starting with the second point, to my amazement, I discovered that Ian and Beatrice Jordan prescribe glasses with coloured lenses at an optical practice called Jordans in Ayr, Scotland. There is no waiting list and appointments are completely free of charge and free of any obligation to purchase glasses. Perfect, definitely worth a try then.

Regarding whether or not coloured lenses would make a difference to my life was solved pretty quickly and conclusively when I saw Ian and Beatrice.

The first test they did on me is called the "Pulfrich" effect. After explaining to me what was going to happen, Ian moved his finger quite quickly towards my nose and then off to one side of my cheek. As promised, at no point did Ian touch my face. However, I jumped a mile in shock – it was one of those instinctive reactions that I could not prevent. My visual processing system and nervous system were telling me that Ian was going to hit me, even though I intellectually knew that he was not, so I flinched. Or more accurately, I did my impression of a very startled horse, shying backwards.

We then compared my reactions when the same test was repeated, but with me looking through red, green and blue filters. We got the same startled, jumping reaction with the red and the blue filters, but I was able to sit there, as cool as a cucumber, when I was looking through the green ones. Hmmm, very bizarre.

We then did a few more tests in a dark room that Ian could illuminate with red light, green light, blue light and, literally, sixteen million colours in between. He tried one where he brought his face very close to mine, again after explaining to me that he was not actually going to touch me at all. In the green, I was completely fine with this. In the blue, his face became like a scary monster on a ghost train – he looked terrifying and I screamed! Me, a then thirty-year old, screaming at an optician… Luckily, although Ian said that other people had not screamed before, he did not take this as a personal insult. We did a few more tests like this, all of which confirmed that green light improved things and red and blue light (particularly blue) made things worse. It is a pity that my colour happens to be green, which has always been one of my least favourite colours, but there we are, we cannot choose our own brains.

I learned from these tests that green filters help me judge distances better. I was jumping and screaming because my eyes were telling me that Ian was going to hit me, when he was actually some distance away from me.

Returning to the front of the opticians, the tests continued. Ian got me to watch him clapping his hands together and asked whether I could hear the clapping at the same time as I could see his hands coming together. Not something I had ever asked myself before. It was a difficult question to answer. I knew I could both see and hear the clapping, but when I really considered the matter, I was not sure about whether it was simultaneous. I eventually realised that I was getting the sight and the sound at slightly different times. In contrast, when I looked though green filters, it definitely was simultaneous – a wholly different experience.

I was beginning to realise that these green filters give me properly integrated visual and auditory senses. This was so strange after having walked into the opticians thinking that I had pretty much near-normal senses. My head was starting to swim and I was feeling like my mouth was permanently stuck in a shocked and gawping expression. The tests continued.

Ian then tested my cognitive ability, by getting me to recite my name and address and also to count backwards from one hundred. I tried it first without wearing any glasses and we repeated the exercises with me looking through the green filters. Now, I would like to assure you that I am intelligent and that I *can* actually say my name and address and count backwards; these are not particularly difficult tasks. However, to my astonishment, everyone present confirmed that I was more fluent in these simple tasks when I was looking through the green filters. Therefore, the green filters also make a cognitive difference; quite literally, they speed my brain up.

We also tested the directionality of my hearing. I stood up, with my back to Ian. Ian then clapped at different places behind my back, for example, behind and to the right of me, behind and to the left, directly behind. Without being able to see where he was, I had to point to the direction that I thought the sound was coming from. "Sure, I should be able to do that", I thought. Wrong! Without the green filters, I had no idea where the sound was coming from and my pointing was random guesswork. However, putting the green filters back in front of my eyes, I *could* tell where the sounds were coming from. That was so strange. So, it seems from this that looking through green filters is not only affecting my sight and my intellectual ability, but is also affecting my hearing.

In conclusion, all of the tests confirmed that I process the colour green well but have some difficulties processing red and blue. My suspicions that I have mild sensory processing difficulties were also confirmed. On a scale of one to ten, one being the least severe and ten being the most severe for sensory processing problems, Ian assessed me as only two out of ten.

Since I process green well, I got some new glasses that are tinted green and they block out a good deal of blue and red light. In appearance, it looks like my lenses were formed from green glass, like the green glass of wine bottles. Some people think they are sunglasses/fashion lenses.

I will now summarise the personal benefits I have received from my green glasses using the following table:

Without my green glasses	With my green glasses
I cannot see and hear at exactly the same time.	I can see and hear at the same time.
I cannot hear the direction a sound comes from.	I can hear the direction a sound comes from.
I flinch when someone's hand passes two inches away from my head.	I am perfectly calm and still when someone's hand passes two inches away from my head.
I do not have very good depth perception and find it hard to walk downstairs.	I have much better depth perception and I am confident walking downstairs.
I get claustrophobic and panicky in crowds, such as in train stations, city centres.	Crowds do not bother me.
I am not perfectly fluent with my speech, even when reciting simple information like my name and address.	My speech has increased fluency, quite noticeable to witnesses.
Fluorescent lights bother me.	I am fine with fluorescent lights.
I am generally tense and uptight.	I am calmer.

Since no-one knows exactly why glasses with coloured lenses work, here is one possible theory. I cannot remember how much of this theory Ian told me compared to how much of it I have deduced through trying to think through logically why the glasses work. However, this is my current understanding:

NTs' brains have a large capacity to process incoming information (sensory information and thoughts), so in general, they have very few processing problems. Their ability to process sensory information and thoughts is *greater* than the amount of information they have to process. This means NTs process sensory information quickly and efficiently and they can use lots of their sensory channels at once. Although NTs probably also have a particular preferred wavelength, it does not make a significant difference for them whether or not they have the glasses, because their brains are already having such an easy time. They do not need coloured glasses.

In contrast, autistic people are a sub-group of people who have a smaller capacity to process incoming information. The ability of autistic people to process sensory information and thoughts is *less* than the amount of information they have to process. Therefore, autistic people find it is most efficient to use a monoprocessing style (only one channel at once).

In the autistic population, the mental effort involved in coping with and processing the full range of colours means that the brain has to devote a lot of its processing capacity to doing this. The brain is like a computer. If a computer is running lots of programs at once, it runs slowly. Thus, if you overload the brain with too many tasks, it also runs slowly.

If your ability to process sensory information and thoughts is *less* than the amount of sensory information and thoughts you have to process, then your brain is forced to take short-cuts. For example, my brain decides to prioritise the processing of sounds. However, it is less important to know from what direction the sounds are coming from, so this task gets skipped. Although I actually have the core ability of being able to distinguish the direction a sound is coming from, I am not able to use this ability when I am overloaded with too much information. Other people might have short-cuts taken in their vision. For example, someone's brain might process the outlines of objects, but not generally process the fine detail of these objects. Such people have to concentrate hard to see the detail in something they are looking at. Some tasks, such as auditory processing, intellectual functioning, vestibular processing, propriosensory processing and pain awareness, may have to take a backseat because there is not enough processing ability left for these other tasks. These tasks might get delayed or not get done at all.

If these tasks are delayed, the delay can range from a fraction of a second to days. In my case, I am slightly delayed on some senses. For example, my sight/sound is mistimed, but only to the order of a fraction of a second. Also, when I am not being brilliantly coherent in reciting my name and address, this is a delay in my intellectual processing of a few seconds. However, some other people have these difficulties to a far greater extent than myself. Some people have such long delays that the experience is unhelpful. For example, some people get very delayed pain. It is not very useful for your learning experience to feel that your hand is hurting *two hours* after burning it on the cooker. It might sound bizarre to you, but some people actually do have such long delays (and even longer). I am not exaggerating! Different people will notice different effects, but I imagine that the root difficulty of not enough processing power is the common cause.

So, okay, we now know that the problem is that autistic people's ability to process sensory information and thoughts is *less* than the amount of sensory information and thoughts they have to process. But what can we do about it?

Well, we cannot alter people's core ability to process information, because this would require brain surgery that has not yet been invented. However, we can alter the other parameter - the amount of information there is to process. This is where the coloured lenses come in.

White light (normal daylight) is made up of red, green and blue light, which are the three primary colours. All of the other colours are made up of mixing together various proportions of red, green and blue light. Yellow = red + green. Purple = red + blue. Turquoise = green + blue. Light is a spectrum of electromagnetic radiation of different wavelengths, blue light being the shortest wavelength, red light being the longest, and the other colours of the rainbow spanning between blue and red. Each individual person's brain finds a different part of the light spectrum easiest to process, for example, in my case, my brain processes green light very efficiently, but struggles with red light and blue light.

Coloured lenses are a way of filtering out particular colours. Using coloured lenses intelligently, we can match the right lens to the right person, so the lens filters out the particular colours that individual finds hardest to process. Green lenses allow green light through whilst blocking red and blue. Blue lenses allow blue light through whilst blocking red and green. Red lenses let red light through whilst blocking green and blue. Yellow lenses let some green and red through, whilst blocking blue.

Since in my particular case, my brain processes green quite well, but struggles with red and blue, I have green coloured lenses, which filter out most of the red and blue light, letting the green through to my eyes. Consequently, when I am wearing my green glasses, my brain does not have to process so much blue or red light, which makes my brain's workload much easier. This allows my brain to (1) work more efficiently, lowering my stress/arousal levels; and (2) perform tasks which it normally would not be able to do, such as hearing the direction a sound is coming from.

So, by reducing the amount of incoming information, your brain is able to do other things that it usually would not have the processing capabilities to do. If your brain is no longer permanently over-stretched, you are calmer and less anxious.

For autistic people, using coloured lenses and therefore excluding a lot of hard-to-process information, can make a huge difference.

Are you eating an orange?

Before getting her glasses, one of my friends thought it was normal to be unable to distinguish her foot from the carpet. She also thought it normal to see trailing lines when a pencil was moved from side to side in front of her face (persistence of vision): "Do you see any trailing lines?" "Only the normal amount".

My friend's daughter has such bad problems with double vision that she thought it was normal to see two television sets instead of just one. She had never mentioned having double vision.

I started clapping my hands repetitively and asked someone if they were seeing the clap at the same time as hearing it. They replied: "Of course not, light travels much faster than sound"! Technically correct of course, but this effect is not noticeable at a distance of fifty centimetres! I know this because of my sensory experiences, but they have always experienced sight and sound at different times, so they believe this is a normal and logical result of light and sound travelling at different speeds! I was rendered quite speechless with shock because I had never predicted this answer and I did not know how to respond.

One of my friends, who can have very delayed sensory experiences, fell through a loft hatch and, despite being bruised all down his body, only realised that he had fallen through once he found himself lying on the floor below. He felt no pain at the time, and took a great interest in pressing his bruises a few days later.

Another friend (who is an experienced driver) cannot see a car properly when it is moving. He sees cars as two-dimensional cardboard cut-outs. When a car turns, there is a different-looking cardboard cut-out (of the side of the car, rather than the rear) and so it does not look like the same car. It is difficult for him to work out if a car is coming towards or away from him. However, the test for good vision for a driving test is to read a stationary number plate at a certain distance - that was no problem for him! Hmmm, something tells me the driving test should be updated…

Glasses with Coloured Lenses

Ian raised his fist and asked my friend how many fingers she saw: "Four". He started wiggling his fingers and asked how many fingers now: "Hundreds; is that not normal?".

"Is that not normal?" is a question which is asked on a daily basis at Jordans!

I would urge everyone on the spectrum to go to Jordans and check this out. Quite a few people (but nowhere near enough) are now getting wise to this, because Ian told me about half of his appointments are for people who travel up to Scotland from England. The Jordans are exceptionally thorough; my assessment took about two hours. Since the appointment is completely free on the NHS, you only pay anything if you decide to purchase glasses. I feel sure that most people on the spectrum will be helped by these lenses. However, even if you do not believe me, you are in a win-win situation, because if they do not help you, you do not have to pay anything. Coloured lenses were yet another thing which I investigated with an open mind, without any particular bias as to whether they would help or not, and with only the knowledge that I was on the spectrum and that coloured lenses had reportedly benefited some other people on the spectrum.

It is important to realise that you cannot tell (without going for an assessment) whether these glasses could benefit you or not. It is not sensible to think "I do not have any visual processing/ sensory problems so the glasses cannot help me". I was not previously aware of any of my visual processing problems that I have described in this chapter. No-one can sit inside anyone else's head to compare experiences in order to judge whether their own perception is "normal" or not. And you would be amazed at the distorted processing that is going on in the heads of some very clever people, who are not remotely aware of it.

Also, please do not think that because your regular optician has not voiced any concerns, this means you do not have this kind of visual processing problem. Regular opticians are assessing the eyes themselves, but the assessment for coloured lenses is testing the brain, not the eyes. In Autism, it is the brain's processing of the sensory information that is more likely to be misleading, rather than the sensory organs themselves. One of my friends had been repeatedly sent for eye tests as a child because it was so obvious to people around her that something was wrong. None of these eye tests ever found any problems and yet she is massively sensitive to some colours of light and has huge sensory distortions.

Since wearing my green glasses in everyday life, it is sometimes difficult to discern exactly how they are helping. I cannot keep repeating my actions with and without the glasses on and asking other people if anything was different. Also, if I am wearing the glasses, my brain should be working better and therefore I should have fewer problems. It is difficult to notice a problem that is not happening. However, they are definitely making my life easier. To me, they seem like magic, calmness glasses (the lower arousal level is very noticeable). Last year, I had to go to hospital after falling off my bike and hurting my shoulder. I was really glad I had the glasses to help me cope with the glare of the lights, the hospital staff being rushed and not explaining things "properly" (on my level), the general confusion, the long wait in the waiting room and the stress of having to get x-rays done. Also, I had to go Christmas shopping one Saturday. Normally, I would do anything to avoid the city centre on a Saturday. I get sort of claustrophobic – confused by trying to process the crowds and hoards of people who are all moving too fast and too close to me. However, part way through a mammoth five-hour shop, I realised that I was not freaked out and was not bothered by the crowds at all. Very weird. Also, I now never walk through my local city centre train station without putting on my glasses. I am also finding it easier to cope with the fluorescent lights at work, piles of autumn leaves and the blue sky. I use my glasses all the time at work, because I need my brain to be functioning at its best and most efficient there. When I am not at work, I choose whether or not to wear them.

Glasses with Coloured Lenses

I do not fully understand the links between Autism, AS, dyspraxia and dyslexia, but there seems to be a big common thread in there somewhere. Perhaps we need a new generic term, for something broader than the Autistic Spectrum – like "the Neurodiversity Spectrum", to encompass these other groups too. The Jordans have a lot of experience in helping people who are dyspraxic and dyslexic as well as those on the autistic spectrum. It seems the brains of people who are dyspraxic and dyslexic also work much more efficiently when certain wavelengths of light are blocked.

I have since recommended these coloured glasses to many of my friends and acquaintances. The people I know personally who have benefited include those with Asperger Syndrome, Autism, dyspraxia, dyslexia, sensory integration dysfunction, magnocellular processing problems, and some with no labels at all.

My dyspraxic friend, who normally only sees in two dimensions, can now see in three dimensions with her new glasses and spends less time tripping over kerbs and furniture. These glasses can help some people walk down corridors without bumping into the walls.

My friend who has prosopagnosia (face blindness) found that using coloured lenses enables her to see her own and other people's faces properly, without distortions. Without her new glasses, she sees people's facial features change in a subtle way that makes her feel different but is hard to describe. Not being able to accurately see facial expressions makes people very vulnerable. Also, if you cannot read faces correctly, it would be easy to misunderstand a social situation. Wearing her new glasses, my friend feels more grounded and less vulnerable. I understand from the Jordans that prosopagnosia is fairly common in people on the spectrum. I have watched a video clip of someone using coloured lenses to see their face for the first time and it is a very beautiful thing. If people who have prosopagnosia get glasses with coloured lenses, they may be more willing to look at someone's face and make eye-contact.

Are you eating an orange?

By prescribing appropriate coloured glasses, Ian and Beatrice report almost invariable successful treatment of metamorphosis (facial distortions), de-synchronisation problems, reduction of facial physical tics of people with Tourettes and many other problems associated with Autism and some other conditions. I also understand that using the right coloured lenses can stop some repetitive stimming (self-stimulatory) behaviours.

My dyslexic friend is now able to see text as much more solid and present upon the page, rather than parts of the text being fainter, as if the ink were running out. My other friend, who is not diagnosed with anything, has stopped seeing "millions of people" when there are only a few people in a shop. My friend's son, who used to write his numbers in mirror-image about 75% of the time, has completely corrected this after four days of wearing his new glasses. My other friend's daughter's reading has improved in leaps and bounds and so has her confidence. I have observed that the glasses can improve some people's processing speed and comprehension of speech. From this, I deduce that many people, with many different labels, areas of difficulty and severity of difficulties, will all benefit from these coloured lenses.

As well as getting the colour correct for the individual, the other difference in people's glasses is how dark they are. The most sensitive people need very dark shades, because these block a higher proportion of the non-preferred colours. However, less sensitive people, such as myself, can get away with lighter shades, which is useful because obviously if things are too dark, it becomes hard to see. Also, very sensitive people need milder versions of the tests that I took in the optician's. Ian is very responsive to this and gives everyone the tests that are appropriate for them.

This sensory stuff, like the Gluten-Free, Casein-Free Diet, is still relatively unknown. I had an enormous amount of stares when I first appeared in my work place, wearing these glasses. In fact, I have never been so stared at in my life; it was like being Harry

Glasses with Coloured Lenses

Potter for the day! But coloured lenses do have really amazing effects and I would advise all auties, aspies, dyslexic and dyspraxic folk to go along and get tested, if you possibly can. For folk with mild sensory issues like me, they make life calmer and easier. For other people, for the first time being able to see a face without distortions, read text clearly and see in three dimensions, is truly life-changing stuff.

I think these glasses are brilliant, but they may not suit everyone. For me, everything is easier with the glasses. But for people with severe sensory issues, wearing the glasses can be overwhelming at first because of being suddenly confronted with a huge amount of visual information they have never seen before and which their brains have never processed. This can be exhausting, confusing and scary. So, the glasses may take some getting used to. It is a good idea to persevere though - perhaps starting off only wearing them for short periods.

Some people might have a problem with the feel of the glasses on their head (again, a sensory issue to be overcome).

Some people may get the glasses, find they help, but then not wear them for fear of standing out and being different. But personally, I found people got used to my glasses pretty quickly and the important thing for me is sorting out my sensory issues, rather than blending into the crowd. I actually get quite a few nice comments from strangers in the street too, who think my glasses are trendy and cool.

Getting glasses with coloured lenses is really important, because it is not necessary to suffer from an imbalanced and overloaded sensory system! If you are on the spectrum, or if you recognise that you have any of the above issues, please check this out. It may just revolutionise your life.

Alexander Technique

According to Jain, Janssen, & DeCelle (2004), four groups of people who particularly benefit from the Alexander Technique are:

1)   people in pain;
2)   athletes/performers;
3)   people with learning disabilities/movement disorders (this .includes people on the autistic spectrum); and
4)   people seeking personal growth.

I discovered the Alexander Technique four years ago, before I knew anything about Autism, when I was trying out various different things in a period of self-development. As a musician, an autistic person and one seeking personal growth, I fall into all of the last three categories, so perhaps my finding the Alexander Technique was not surprising. Furthermore, since my posture used to be pretty awful, if I had not started the Alexander Technique when I did, it is probable that I would have ended up in the first category too before very much longer.

So, what is the Alexander Technique? This is simple to understand when you experience an Alexander lesson, but rather complicated to explain in words. Nevertheless, I shall try. The Alexander Technique is a "somatic education technique designed to establish heightened awareness of movements" (Jain, Janssen, & DeCelle, 2004, p. 811). Essentially, instead of relying on feedback from your propriosensory system (which may be inaccurate) to position or move your body, the Alexander Technique uses touch from the Alexander teacher to indicate how the body should be moved or held. The Alexander Technique uses a direct, hands-on approach from the practitioner to help define movements objectively and to reposition the student. The student is encouraged to use visual cues to maintain positioning rather than just proprioception, so that he does not rely entirely on misleading proprioceptive feedback (Jain et al., 2004). Alexander found that habitual misuse of his body affected his kinesthetic (proprioceptive) sense and he continually stressed the importance of accurate sensory appreciation (Gelb, 1981).

I found the Alexander Technique to be remarkably good for me, as an autistic person, which got me wondering if any research/ scientific papers had been done, linking Autism and the Alexander Technique. I searched hard, but only found one reference to both Autism and the Alexander Technique, this being Tinbergen (1973). Tinbergen (a Nobel Prize winner for his work in the field of animal behaviour) devoted his Nobel Prize acceptance speech to a discussion of the two topics of "early infantile Autism" and the Alexander Technique (Tinbergen, 1973); very odd themes for an animal behaviour specialist to choose! However, far from praising this speech, both his biographer, Hans Kruuk, and John Krebs, who reviewed Tinbergen's biography, thought this speech would "best be forgotten" (Krebs, 2004, p. 294). Barlow (1976) claims that Tinbergen's speech advocated the use of the Alexander Technique to alleviate early infantile Autism, but from my reading of the speech, this is incorrect. In my opinion, Tinbergen discusses Autism and the Alexander Technique as two separate and distinct themes.

Tinbergen (1973) describes the Alexander Technique as a very gentle corrective manipulation of the entire muscular system and explains how the technique is based on observation, by vision and touch. Tinbergen also explains Alexander's idea that the lifelong misuse of the body (for example, by too much sitting and too little walking) can make the body go wrong. The brain gets reports that all is correct, when this is not so. For example, a person slouching in front of the TV feels fine although his body is misaligned.

Jain et al. (2004) found few blinded and controlled studies of the Alexander Technique published in peer-reviewed journals. One difficulty is how to conduct blind testing with this very "hands-on" technique. A "blind test" means that the person being tested does not know that they are being tested on. It is pretty much impossible to be learning the Alexander Technique without knowing that you are learning it!

I have now been taking Alexander classes for four years. During this time, I have experienced some amazing changes. Firstly, my posture is much improved. My parents and dance teacher were always telling me not to slouch, but because of my unreliable proprioceptive sense, lax joints and uncoordinated body, I was unable to do this. When I tried to sit/stand up straight, I would over-tense many muscles to achieve this, which rapidly resulted in a great deal of pain, so I stopped trying. Now after many lessons, my spine is much straighter, which means my internal organs are no longer so cramped up inside my body. I can now breathe more easily, which gives my brain more oxygen, so I feel more alert, more comfortable and happier.

My speech is now slower and more comprehensible than it used to be, but *not* because I have made an effort to change my speech in any way. My boss at work had previously told me on a number of occasions that I spoke too quickly, but as I had no awareness of this, I was not able to slow down. However, I eventually managed to slow my speech down as a by-product of the Alexander Technique. This was how it happened. One lesson, my Alexander teacher told me that I was shaking my head vigorously every time I said the word "no" and nodding my head just as enthusiastically every time I said the word "yes". This was news to me! She said that when I talked, I was bouncing my head around on the top of my spinal column, like a balloon on a stick. Perhaps my speech was fast because I was rushing to get a lot of words out before my next head bounce. I do not know because I was not aware of it. My teacher simply asked me to concentrate on not shaking my head when I said "no". I was not willing to do this at first, because I thought that being expressive was nice and I did not want to change this aspect of myself. However, my teacher argued that it was not okay to be waving my head around without being consciously aware I was doing this and that I would get neck/back problems if I continued. This was enough to convince me that this was a habit to lose! Hence, for the next two weeks, I paid a lot of attention to inhibiting shaking my head whenever I said "no". This took a lot of effort. First, I had to try to notice when I was shaking my head and think: "oops, there I go again". Then, I had to notice before the impulse to shake my head and actually prevent myself doing my habitual head-shake. However, I was very determined to eliminate this habit, which I managed within about two weeks. In my next Alexander lesson, my teacher told me that I was talking much slower! So, my slower talking was an accidental by-product of reducing my head movement and was achieved without trying to slow my speech down at all!

Even more astoundingly, my mental state has much improved since practising the Alexander Technique. Before starting Alexander classes, I was usually stuck in the thinking channel, having a lot of repetitive thoughts and being relatively cut off from the outside world for large portions of my life. My monoprocessing style meant that whilst I was thinking, I was not aware of anything else, so I did not tend to take much notice of my senses. My Alexander teacher encourages me to be aware of sensory information. In the Alexander lesson, there is propriosensory, tactile and visual information to work with. I now consciously practise trying not to think and to instead stick on the visual or auditory channels when I take a walk. It seems funny that in school, we are encouraged to think more, whereas now I find myself really struggling to do the exact opposite. And there is an inherent contradiction; because of my aspie-status, I have to do a lot more conscious thinking than NTs. I have varying degrees of success at staying away from the thinking channel and it does involve quite a lot of conscious effort. When I get stressed beyond a certain threshold, this is impossible and I cannot leave the confines of my head.

Another strange consequence is that, just after leaving an Alexander class, I find that I am very aware of my surroundings, *without consciously trying to be* and, for a few seconds, I feel what it must be like to have well-integrated senses. Perhaps with further practice, this effect will become more long-lasting. This leads me to consider Alexander Technique as a type of sensory integration therapy.

I found the literature to be almost non-existent in regards to the Alexander Technique as an intervention for autistic people (as I said above, I do not believe the Tinbergen lecture counts because the topics were unconnected). Therefore, I will need to give you my own theories as to why the Alexander Technique is such a good intervention.

I think the key is understanding that, in people on the spectrum, propriosensory feedback/motor clumsiness is likely to be a weakness. This is known from many sources. For example, the diagnostic criteria lists motor clumsiness as a usual, but not a necessary diagnostic feature of AS (ICD-10, 1994).

Miyahara et al. (1997) found that of twenty-six aspies, 85% had a motor function disorder. Similarly, Green et al. (2002) studied eleven aspies and found all met the criteria for a diagnosis of motor impairment. Minshew et al. (2004) found that development of postural stability is delayed in autistic subjects and never reaches normal adult levels. They also found problems with multimodal sensory integration. Molloy, Dietrich & Bhattacharya (2003) found children with ASD to have a lesser postural stability, consistent with a deficit in integration of visual, vestibular and somatosensory input to maintain postural orientation. Molloy et al. (2003) concluded that a proprioceptive deficit was the most likely cause.

For myself, I definitely have proprioceptive problems (see sensory chapters) and I am sure that most or all of the above all applies to me.

The Alexander Technique helps with these problems by using feedback from three modes (visual, tactile and propriosensory) instead of just relying on the accuracy of the propriosensory system (we noted above how Alexander stressed the importance of accurate sensory feedback). Furthermore, the tactile input in the Alexander Technique is reliable because it is delivered by an objective teacher. The teacher guides the student into an upright alignment of the head, neck and back and also guides movements of the student whilst maintaining this same relationship of head, neck and back. When my teacher adjusts my body position, it usually feels "wrong" because she is putting me into a position that is not normal for me. I might feel that I am leaning backwards a lot or sticking my bum out. However, when I turn and look at myself in the mirror, I find that I am actually really straight and upright. This is a case of my propriosensory system giving the wrong answer, but the touch from my Alexander teacher providing the correct alignment.

My experience is that my body is like a too-floppy wooden Pinocchio puppet, where the bits of string connecting the wooden limbs are a bit too loose. I compensate for this by tensing too many muscles, too tightly, effectively grabbing hold of my body parts to make them go where I need them to. Marc Segar (undated) said: "Autistic people have to understand scientifically what non-autistic people already understand instinctively." I would extend this principle to: "Autistic people also have to consciously do some things which non-autistic people already do instinctively". Whilst aspies such as myself do not intuitively use our bodies well, we can learn to control our bodies better, consciously. Indeed, one of Alexander's books is entitled: "Constructive, conscious control of the individual", and that is precisely what the Alexander Technique achieves. And it certainly is conscious. I do not know any NTs who need to concentrate when they walk, to make sure their heel goes down before the rest of the foot, to avoid flat-footed, heavy, clumpy walking.

Are you eating an orange?

I find the Alexander Technique to be great, but it is not suitable for people who are tactile defensive (do not like being touched). Yoga is a good supplementary or alternative activity, which can achieve some of the same things and which does not involve being touched.

As an (I think fascinating) aside, after reading Alexander's biography (Bloch, 2004), my opinion is that Alexander himself was an aspie. According to Bloch he: was clever; highly strung; had "violent internal pains" (p. 22) (intestinal problems from eating gluten?); had a good rote memory (learned Shakespearean monologues by heart and got a job as a reciter); was independent and industrious; pursued his goals single-mindedly; had a strong moral sense; his interests were "obsessions" (p. 27); he felt like an outsider; liked plain speaking; suffered from social isolation; in public, he acted a part and could not afford to let his mask slip; he had supporters rather than intimate friends; he was a loner; he refused to join clubs or attend parties; he was lonely; he described true happiness as "doing well the things that interest one" (p. 125); his marriage lacked intimacy; Lucie Westfeldt thought he was a bad teacher who could not understand what went on in the minds of others; his Technique was utterly original to him (derived from first principles); he could not do small talk; and only his mother really understood him. He also has a deliberately averted eye gaze in all the photos in the book - it is strikingly unusual. Furthermore, Alexander believed that unreliable sensory appreciation was a universal phenomenon (quite naturally, he assumed that he was normal), however, this belief was questioned in Alexander's libel case against the South African government. Also, the very thing which prompted him to devise the Technique was his voice failing him when reciting, as a consequence of his own poor posture.

I think Alexander being autistic (and avoiding social functions, networking and advertisement of his Technique even to the point of refusing the help of his admirers to do this when handed to him on a plate) is one of the reasons this incredible therapy is still very marginalised and relatively unknown today. Another case of not *what* you know, but *who* you know.

There you go, one of my cases of aspie-spotting and one of my most surprising findings.

Autism and the Criminal Justice System

I freely admit that I am not the world's greatest authority on Autism and the criminal justice system; however, this is such an important (and under-recognised) topic that I thought I should include a chapter on it, based on my experiences. I am not writing this chapter because crime is one of the major issues in my life. It probably is not. On a day-to-day basis, I have far more difficulty in getting along in the work place. And I completely admit I have been lucky in quite a few of the cases described below, so nothing really bad has happened to me. However, in reading this, please try to use your imagination to think what could happen to someone less high functioning than myself (and, if I am honest with you, just someone who was less lucky than I have been so far), and you might then start to get a glimpse of the importance of this issue to the autistic population as a whole.

I have found it surprisingly difficult to find published statistics of how many people in prison (or other parts of the criminal justice system) are on the spectrum. I thought there would be a generally-agreed percentage that I could find and quote for you. However, this does not seem to be the case. The various studies which have been done seem to come up with very different estimates of the prevalence of people with ASD who are in prison. Allen et al (2008) suggested that the lack of accurate prevalence figures of ASD in the population as a whole made it difficult to determine whether people on the spectrum in prison were over- or under-represented compared to the general population. However, they did conclude that most people with a diagnosis of Asperger Syndrome "who do fall foul of the law clearly struggle to negotiate the criminal justice system". Therefore, whether it eventually turns out that we are over-represented in the criminal justice system or not, what is clear is that at least some aspies and auties are in prison or are otherwise involved in the criminal justice system. This alone merits the inclusion of this chapter.

My gut feeling, largely from extrapolating from my own personal experience and from what I know about the difficulties of life on the spectrum, is that we *are* more likely to be in prison than the average person (whoever that is) and we are more likely to be victims of crime or witnesses to it. I will discuss examples of all of the above in this chapter. I freely acknowledge that I am not qualified to tell you this is definitely the case. This is just my personal theory.

So, how does anyone on the spectrum end up in prison? At a first consideration, this seems odd. We are nature's rule-followers and many of us are extremely moral. I suspect the reasons are complex. One reason for an autistic person committing a criminal act might be if they are told to do it by someone else. Many autistic people are trained to comply, in the absence of understanding what is going on, so some of us are very easily led. Also, I could very easily picture a situation where an autie/aspie is out shopping, they are holding an item, the sensory overload (music, fluorescent lights, crowds, smells) becomes too much, they try to escape from the shop as quickly as possible to avoid a meltdown/shutdown and they run out of the shop still holding the item. Thus, accidental shop-lifting could easily occur, when only self-preservation from unbearable sensory-assault was intended. There will also be many other reasons, in addition to these ones above.

I will now talk about some of my own experiences with crime and the criminal justice system.

Victim of Crime

Autistic people have an increased risk of being victims of crime because we have a fundamental, lesser all-round awareness than most people have. This includes a lesser awareness of danger. Whilst we are focusing down our narrow attention tunnels, bad stuff can happen to us. Gestalt perception, monoprocessing and perpetual information overload are the cause of this problem.

Are you eating an orange?

Once, I had my handbag stolen in a pub, when I put it down between my chair and the wall. Our table was in the corner of the pub. I was concentrating on the conversation and did not notice someone coming up behind me, taking my bag and walking away with it.

On a separate occasion, I had my watch stolen off my wrist, without noticing. This happened in an airport and I can time the theft pretty precisely because I had only just adjusted my watch to take account of the time difference. Five minutes later, I tried to look at my watch and it was gone. However, I was totally unaware of the actual theft.

On many occasions, I have had lucky escapes due to my impressive ability to get lost and my very small ability to sense danger. Once, I left a night club and tried to walk home but I went in the wrong direction. I ended up in the red light district where all the prostitutes hung out. It was about 1:00am and I did feel a bit worried, but I was not sure how to get back to the city centre. Luckily, a car was passing by, driving very slowly with the window open and I asked for directions back to the city centre. Only the next day at work (when I was telling everyone else about this particular adventure and how lucky I was that the car just happened to be there) was I prompted by my colleagues to realise just what the man was doing, driving his car slowly through the red light district at 1:00am... that totally had not occurred to me!

On other occasions, due to my tendency to avoid crowded places, I can sometimes be found wandering through back streets by myself. People have told me that this is a bad idea, but without actually feeling the sense of danger myself, it is very easy to ignore this advice, especially when a counter-benefit is available, for example, not having to pay for a taxi or getting away from being overwhelmed by crowds/noise/movement/traffic. Yes, I do know this is stupid. However, I still sometimes do this.

On a different occasion, I had (what I hope is) a very narrow escape from being the victim of ID fraud. I received a phone call at home, from a woman who asked to speak to me but used "Mrs" instead of "Miss". My first thought was that this was probably a sales call. However, the woman then told me that she was phoning from the city council about a mistake that had been made in the council tax banding of my flat. She said my flat had been wrongly classified in error and I was due a refund of the money I had been over-charged since I moved into my flat. I was really pleased to hear that and started to think of how to calculate the correct proportion to refund to my last flatmate. The woman said the easiest way would be to refund the money onto a debit or credit card and I agreed to that. She then asked for the name written on the card and my date of birth, both of which I gave her. She then asked for the expiry date of my debit card and warning bells started to ring in my head. I told her I was not comfortable giving that information over the telephone and could she please write to me about this matter instead. She then said some things that confused me; that the refund was automatically going to happen anyway, but if I wanted to get the claim form and file it myself as a paper copy, it was going to cost ninety-nine pounds. She told me that she was definitely not a fraud person, because a fraud person would be asking for my account number and sort code and she was not asking for these things. She also told me that she knew I banked with the particular bank I do use (I had not disclosed the name of the bank to her) and that she could only know that because she was from the city council and had my direct debit information.

This was really starting to confuse me and I still did not feel comfortable about it. I still thought it might be a genuine call (perhaps this person had not been trained properly) but I had expected some proper reassurance about the security of giving my details over the phone. I thought she might have suggested for me to call her back through the council switchboard, for example. So, I asked to speak to her supervisor, who did not make the situation seem any clearer. I put the phone down. I then phoned my Dad and told him what had happened. I said I thought it was possibly a fraud call and he said that of course it was a fraud call and that I should have hung up the telephone much sooner than I actually did. I then called my bank and told them that some of my details had been compromised. They told me to destroy my debit and credit cards straight away and they issued new ones. I also phoned the police, who could only give me general advice and could not put a trace on the call or anything because "a crime has not been committed until money is actually stolen from you and we cannot do anything until a crime has been proved to have been committed". The policeman was not very comforting when he said: "I am surprised this has happened to you; it is normally old people who have this problem". So, I told him that I was autistic and a vulnerable member of the public, thank you very much!

The whole experience was extremely scary and it made me feel very stupid that I had taken quite a long time to catch on to the fact that the call was dodgy and that I had given them some of my personal details before I had caught on. It made me feel unsafe and made me question my ability to look after myself. I was shocked that this nice-sounding woman was trying to steal from me. I actually felt like I had been abused (although this was only a telephone call) because I had been open and trusting and they had been lying. The scariest thing was I did not feel the matter was over, because of possible repercussions of what might happen to me now, as a result. I did not know (and am still not sure) whether these people will try to make purchases or open accounts in my name, because they certainly seemed to be building up a database of information about me.

The Autism-related points to this story include:

1.   Slow information processing (leading to literal thinking) and my own lack of deception-related skills results in my believing what people say. I am good at dealing with sales calls such as: "do you want a chance to win a holiday?" because these are honest

and I can say "no". However, I was completely unprepared for someone calling me on the telephone, in my own home, and telling a pack of lies. I am still shocked by this now.

2.   Slow information processing meant that I did not have the mental space during that telephone call to realise some things did not make sense. For example, if the woman was really from the city council, she would have known that I am not a "Mrs"; and the fact that you do not need to know someone's date of birth in order to process a payment into their account. I was able to realise these things later, but not at the time, because being overloaded with incoming information hinders simultaneous processing of this information for significance.

3.   Having a brain structure that is larger and heavier than NTs' brains but with lots of side streets for communication routes rather than motorways, meant that although I did *know* the rule that you should not give out personal details over the telephone, it took me a long time to *access* that rule. So, even the knowledge I did have was not accessible to me quickly enough, in a real-time interaction, whilst I was being distracted through having to work hard to process the incoming information.

4.   Having less common sense and general knowledge than most people, I had to ask my Dad for the next steps (phone the bank and phone the police).

Witness to Crime, Part 1: the event

I have only one personal example of this, but it raises quite a number of relevant points so I think it is worth telling the story.

Once upon a time, it was a beautiful midsummer's evening, around 9:00pm, and I went to sit on a bench in my local park. Since it was midsummer, it was still very light and there were a fair number of people still in the park, although none in the particular area that

Are you eating an orange?

I was, up at the top of the hill next to the flagpole. I was sitting on a bench, enjoying the peace and quiet, asking God if he actually existed or not and asking for some kind of sign. I am hoping what happened next was not the sign.

A man came up to the flagpole. I remember that he was dragging a wheelie suitcase and holding a pop bottle. He asked if he could sit down on the bench next to me. I said yes. I went back to waiting for my sign from God. He then asked me how old I was. So I told him. Since this was the sort of question that sounded like it needed to be reciprocal, I then asked how old he was. He said thirty-two. OK, fine. Then, he slumped down on the bench and started to unbuckle his trousers, simultaneously saying "So, do you want some then?" At this point, I leapt up off the bench like a rocket and started briskly heading down the hill. "No, thanks," I told him, keeping moving. He sounded surprised and disappointed and said "Oh, are you sure?". I told him that I was quite sure and hurried off home. He did not try to restrain me, he had not threatened me in any way and I was completely unharmed, but I still felt a little shaken up.

This happened before I got my diagnosis of Autism. Now, with my diagnosis, I am pretty sure that someone else would have picked up some signals that this person was "dodgy" a long, long time before I did. I was first aware there was something wrong when the man started to take off his trousers. I am pretty sure that I missed a lot of body language/appearance issues that would have immediately rang warning bells to an NT. For instance, I did think it was a bit unusual that a complete stranger was asking how old I was, but I took this for his way of making conversation and thought maybe he was a bit lonely. Being slow to sense danger/ when things are wrong, puts us at a greater risk of being a victim/ witness to crime.

Witness to Crime, Part 2: the aftermath

The following Monday, I told this story to some people at work and they all told me that I should go to the police. I did not see the point of that, since I could not remember what the man looked like, so I did not think I could be any help to them. However, I gave it a shot and phoned the police the following weekend. To my surprise, they took my call quite seriously and were round at my flat that same evening. I told them everything I could remember but said I did not think I could remember what the man looked like. I could not even answer questions like was he tall or short, or what colour hair he had. I told them about the pop bottle and said that it was possible that the bottle contained alcohol but I did not know. They then asked me if I had been drinking myself, because they said it was very strange that I had no recollection of the man's appearance. I said no, and that I had only had half a pint of cider at lunchtime, eight or nine hours previously. Since I did not yet have my diagnosis, I could not explain to them why I did not know what this man looked like. Now, I realise this was:

1.   Because of my narrow attention tunnel - I was predominantly using the thinking and listening channels at the time;

2.   Because I am very much an auditory thinker, not a visual thinker - I could recall everything he said to me and I said to him, but hardly any visual details; and

3.   Because of being autistic, I process faces as if they are objects, instead of with a face-specialised part of my brain.

However, because at the time, I did not have my diagnosis and was not aware of these issues, I could not explain to the police why I had no idea what this person looked like, and their assumption was that I was perhaps drunk. Later in this same conversation, the policemen were taking my details and as part of that, asked what my job was. When I told them it was something quite high flying, they both abruptly stared at me in shock. I think they had me pegged down as some weirdo flaky person who got drunk in parks.

The policemen then came back on another occasion with sixteen photographs and asked if I recognised any of them. To my very great surprise, one of them did look familiar. The other fifteen definitely did not. I was pretty sure that man was the one. However, later that day, I was suddenly struck by the thought that I might have just thought he looked similar to someone I had seen on television! I did think I recognised the man in the photograph; however, I was not at all sure where I recognised him from… On balance, it was probably not a famous television personality and it probably was the man I met in the park, but I did feel a bit concerned.

Some time passed and I then received a letter from the Sheriff Court, saying that the man I had identified was going to be tried for "Breach of the Peace". There had apparently been other incidents (which was why his face was included in the sixteen photographs the police had). I was called as a witness. The letter was very brief and just told me the date of the trial, the name of the court, the accused person's name and that I had to appear. One day before the trial, I had still not received any further information (contrary to stated in the letter), so I had to telephone the court to confirm that I was still required.

On the day of the trial, I arrived at 9:00am, on my bike. Up until this point, I was not remotely concerned because I had not had the imagination or the foresight to think what was going to happen. The Sheriff's Court building was very imposing - a grey stone citadel monstrosity. There was a big wall and a eight foot drop on the other side of the wall, a bit like a moat. There was airport-style security just inside the building. Before I had even passed the security, I felt like I was a criminal myself. I felt guilty and scared of even being in the building. I asked for directions, found the lift and managed to find the waiting room. The waiting room was very crowded, as it was filled with other witnesses, a bit like a doctor's surgery. There was no natural light. I had to register at a desk. They told me they did not know when my case would be called and I would just have to wait. There were boards up around the room, with names of the accused people on them. I concluded this was not a very nice way of being called as a witness - to have to respond to your accuser's name being called. For me, it did not matter because the actual "crime" had not bothered me very much. But it cannot be very nice for rape victims to have to answer to their rapist's name. The name of my accused person was not included on any of the boards, even though it should have been and no-one was very clear about what this meant. Had they forgotten about the trial I had been called to? Was it really happening? I was just told to wait.

Whilst waiting, a woman from a charity came to talk to me. She explained some of what was going to happen in the court room. She drew a map of the room and started talking to me about who the people were going to be and their different jobs. I cannot remember the details, but it was something like a judge, a court reporter, members of the public, the accused man, the witness box (where I was meant to be) and two lawyers, one for the prosecution and one for the defence. She explained that I was going to be cross-examined by both of these lawyers. She also warned me not to trip up the step on my way into the witness box. Now, I know this will sound really stupid and obvious to you, but none of this had occurred to me. I just thought I would be asked some questions, but I did not know that this would be from two different people, cross-examining me. When this woman left, I started to panic, big-time. I really was not sure of my facts. I was worried that I was not going to know the answers to the questions, mostly based on how very hazy/almost non-existent my recollection of the man's appearance was. I was worried that I might try to guess my answer and that an innocent person might end up in prison because I guessed wrong. And now I was additionally worried about tripping over the step and trying to work out who everyone was in the court-room.

I continued to wait. Normally, when I get anxious about something, a big surge of adrenalin builds up, but then after the event is over it can die away. However, because there was no given time for the trial to occur "wait until you are called", I could not time my anxiety right and I remained in fever-pitch anxiety for two or three hours. I tried to read but could not properly concentrate. The longer I waited, the worse a state I got into. Eventually, I phoned a friend just because I was so scared. I waited more. When my accused person's name was called, I was about ready to faint and I had a bit of trouble standing up and walking over to the reception area. However, when I got there, I was told that my accused person had not shown up and that I was free to go. I left the building, and went to collect my bike, thinking: "oh no, after all that, I might have to come back and go through this all over again another day". I got on my bike and tried to cycle to work (a very short distance away). However, within about thirty seconds, I realised I had to stop cycling because I was still in such a state of panic and shock that it was like my eyes were not working. I was a complete danger and menace on the road because I was not seeing the traffic properly. So, I got off and walked with my bike back to work.

So, what went wrong here?

1.   My poor ability to recognise faces or remember what the man in the park looked like, meant that I was a very bad witness. Feeling very unsure about being able to identify the person made me very anxious that I might give the wrong responses and cause a miscarriage of justice. Being autistic but undiagnosed meant that I could not explain this.

2.   The court procedure was completely lacking in clarity and proper explanations. The letter I received told me the date of the trial, the address of the court and the accused person's name but nothing else. It was completely lacking in any procedural information (what will happen, map of the court, timetable, who I will have to speak to). This was a particular problem for me

because of my difficulties with imagination; I had not managed to make any correct assumptions about what I was about to face, other than I knew someone was going to ask me some questions.

3.   When I did receive some of this information, in the waiting room on the day of the trial, this was far too late. This initiated full-scale panic systems. It is very difficult to take in information in a state of worry and panic.

4.   Not being given a time for this trial to take place meant that I was on an extremely high anxiety level for two or three hours, non-stop. I am much more able to cope with a difficult situation if I know exactly when it is going to happen. "Wait until we call you" meant that it could happen at any time and my anxiety went through the roof and stayed that way.

The very great irony of all of this, is that I was almost unfazed by the original incident in the park. However, I was utterly *traumatised* (to the extent of having the worst panic attack of my entire life) by showing up for the trial, which never actually even took place. I found myself wishing that I had never gone to the police in the first place, although morally, I suppose it was the right thing to have done. The criminal justice system has a very long way to go if taking part in it *in any form, even as a witness to a crime that was not itself upsetting*, is not meant to traumatise autistic people.

Perpetrator of crime

I hasten to add, that I did not actually commit the crime I am about to tell you about, but I very nearly did. And this is *me*, little goody-two shoes; it quite surprised me how close I came.

Recently, I bought a top from a clothes shop, but later, when I started wearing it, I discovered some loops on it and concluded it was probably missing a belt. A few weeks later, I was passing the same shop and went in to check. Sure enough, all other tops like mine had a belt. Since I had not planned on entering the shop that day, I did not have my purchase receipt with me. However, I considered that in all fairness one of these belts belonged to me, since my top was missing a belt. I did not want to have to bother to remember to go home and come back another day with the receipt. I decided just to take one of these other belts and put it in my pocket. I was on the point of doing this, when I suddenly remembered the existence of security cameras and I realised the risk I would be running of getting caught. I then realised, with a shock, that what I was about to do was actually shoplifting and what a stupid risk that would be, for the sake of something that probably was worth around one pound.

This example highlights that I am strongly directed to do things by my internal moral compass, rather than by other people's morality/society's rules. I would never dream of stealing something from a shop just because I wanted it. The only reason I nearly did it this time, was that I considered that morally, the belt I would be taking already belonged to me. It was only by some very quick thinking (that nearly did not happen) that I realised how stupid it would have been to have taken that belt. If I was less high-functioning or less intelligent (or even just more dopey on that particular day), then I could easily have committed that crime.

In the criminal justice system and hospitals

I am extremely keen to stay out of both the criminal justice system and hospitals, if at all possible. Obviously, I realise no-one wants to go to these places. However, for me, they would present additional problems that NTs would not have. In particular, I would have the very serious concerns that none of these institutions, at the present, are developed enough to take care of me properly - and certainly not as well as I can take care of myself if I remain independent.

Particular aspie-related problems I would have if arrested would include:

1.   being hand-cuffed and therefore having someone in my personal space - too much people-contact;

2.   sharing a cell with another prisoner - too much people-contact;

3.   the uncertainty of when, exactly, I will be called for trial - lack of predictability causing major stress and anxiety issues and mental health breakdown;

4.   the breakdown of my usual routines - loss of calm;

5.   the impossibility of continuing my Gluten-Free Casein-Free Diet (everyone has to eat what they are given) leading to stomach cramps, bad gut problems and pain which makes me think I am going to faint, impaired functioning and weight-loss. Since this gut problem is not diagnosed by a doctor, I do not believe I would get any concessions towards this;

6.   the lack of access to my usual support people/systems - mental health breakdown;

7.   possible bullying by other prisoners - major stress and mental health breakdown.

These are just ones I can think of off the top of my head (never having actually been arrested myself), so the list might be far greater. From what I understand, being put into an institution/ any kind of hospital where you are kept in against your will, would have a lot of the same problems as being in prison, with the massive disadvantage that, unlike prisoners and failed asylum-seekers, autistic people in institutions cannot get legal aid. In this way, being in an institution is actually a worse position than being a criminal, with the unfairness that you can be put into an institution without committing any crime. I know this might sound really extreme, but this actually does happen with alarming frequency to people on the spectrum - one case was reported in the October 2009 edition of Asperger United (The National Autistic Society, 2009). That story is truly shocking, starting off with the person retaliating against people who were bullying him at work and ending up with him sectioned and drugged up in an institution and being told that he was evil because "autistic people cannot understand how other people feel, so are more likely to attack them".

For me to stay well, I need my Gluten-Free, Casein-Free Diet, my green glasses, my exercise, my routines and structured work and free time, my freedom, access to my interests, access to my important people and the ability to get away from people to prevent overload. I also need to stay off drugs (in which I include illegal drugs, anti-psychotics and the drug-like effects of gluten and casein), which is another reason I very much want to stay out of hospitals. For all these reasons, I have to work particularly hard to take care of myself to avoid the criminal justice system and hospitals. But very few people can avoid a hospital/nursing home all their lives, so I am really wanting to highlight these fundamental needs. I very much hope that before this happens to me, the world has listened to the importance of not drugging autistic people for their "behaviours" and the right to be on the Gluten-Free, Casein-Free Diet in prisons and hospitals, whether or not one's doctor happens to see the need for it or not.

Life-Balance

The way I see it, the more you have in your life, the less you are likely to crumble if any one thing gets taken away from you. Many people base their self-esteem in one or more of the following things: youth, beauty, having a partner, their children, health, work, having money, being good at their job, their family/friend relationships. However, all of these things are intransient and can be taken away. Therefore, it seems to me that the most secure and well-balanced people either base their self-esteem in something more permanent and/or play a number of different roles in their lives. It stands to reason that if the only thing you do in your life is work and sleep and then you lose your job, you are likely to be in a mental mess. However, if you are a daughter, a mother, a singer, a dancer, a friend and an employee, and then you lose your job, whilst you still may have a bit of a lousy time, you are more likely to be in a better condition mentally, because although you have lost one role, you still have the others.

This is all about leading a "balanced life". I have to say this is very hard for aspies and auties to do - balance does not come naturally to me, because I have a very focussed, one-track mind. If I am doing something, I want to do it as well as possible and I put a lot of effort into that. For example, when I sit exams, I study very intensely, often to the exclusion of many other activities. This approach has meant that I have never failed an exam. However, I notice that other people do not tend to let studying take over their entire lives and they manage to maintain relationships and generally have a more chilled out time. I do see the advantages of this approach. However, even with this understanding, I do not think I would be able to study any other way. I do not think I could be happy with myself if I was doing something with only 50% effort.

Therefore, I can certainly admire the benefits, but I am not sure that the NT "balanced life" would work for me in practice. However, there may be a different kind of balance that spectrum folk can achieve. It works more in series than in parallel and concerns doing things sequentially. If you cannot split your energy into 33% work, 33% friendships and fun, 33% relationships, what you can do is 100% all the time, directed at different activities sequentially. For example, for the last while, I have been concentrating on my career and using the money earned to buy a flat and pay off my mortgage. Now that the mortgage is paid off, I have a part-time job and with the extra time and energy I hope to socialize more and perhaps start a relationship. Hopefully, later on, I can have children and either work part-time or not at all and concentrate on bringing up the children. I realize this is not what most people would call balanced, but this might be more realistic for me. This path takes account of my perfectionism and how hard I try to do things. This path also includes easing up in some areas of my life, to enable other areas to develop. As to whether this will work or not, you will have to wait for my next book!

One thing that gets in the way of my own balance is anxiety. If I am trying hard to solve a problem in one area of my life, this preoccupies my mind and I feel like my life is on hold until I have sorted it out. An example of this was buying my flat. I really struggled with the uncertainty of not knowing exactly when I would find a place that I liked and get my offer accepted. I did not have any solution to my anxiety problem, except to try to sort out the flat buying as soon as possible, which would end the anxiety. Also, flats were selling so quickly at the time, that if you did not manage to view a flat in the first few days that it was on the market, it could be sold before you could even see it. However, the harder I worked at searching for and viewing flats, the more exhausted I got from not being able to have a balanced life whilst flat-hunting so hard. It was a trade-off between the anxiety of the uncertainty of the future and between working myself too hard trying to find a flat which caused a lot of stress and exhaustion.

Life-Balance

One of the difficult things I find about attaining balance is getting the level of sociability just right. If I am too sociable and too busy, I can get exhausted and overloaded. However, if I am on my own too much, I can feel sad, lonely and bored and think too many negative thoughts. Sometimes, it feels like living on a knife edge in that I tend to be in one or other of these two states and I flip between them as I adjust what I do, trying to get the level right. In the past, I often strived so hard to avoid loneliness that I took on too many things and felt exhausted.

I would assume that NT folk also have this issue, but for them, I feel the width is different. For NTs there seems to be a road's width in the middle, where they are happy in quite a wide tolerance band. With people on the spectrum, it is not a road, it is a knife edge. Also, the NT road is generally much further towards the sociable end of the scale than the autistic knife edge.

One thing which has definitely made my knife edge blunter (and therefore a bit wider although still not a road) is improving my self-esteem. For this, I can thank a whole combination of people and things, including the Alexander Technique, my church, my friends, dancing, choir and learning about Autism. Although all of these have played a part, possibly the most important has been the Alexander Technique and learning about Autism. The Alexander Technique was what calmed my mind down and took away a lot of the racing, repetitive and negative thoughts. Now that a lot of those are cleared away, being by myself is much easier to cope with.

Autism-Friendly Activities

Activities are great because I am not brilliant at small talk and so it is sometimes easier to talk to folk if it is about a topic of interest, such as the activity in question. Activities/hobbies are also a good way of meeting people that you otherwise would not meet, and a great help in making new friends.

Over the last few years, I have added personal-development stuff to my general activities, by which I mean I have been trying something new every six months or so. I am really pleased with this approach and I find that I am now a lot happier than I was five years ago. If you do not try something, you will never know if you like it.

The first thing I tried was an assertiveness course. I would like to be able to say that I am now very assertive. Unfortunately, this is not true, but I do have a better insight into why people behave as they do. I understand the principles, but my attempts at assertiveness can backfire in practice, where I can be taken for blunt/rude or even angry, when I am simply trying to make a polite request. I think you need a very high level of social skill to be assertive successfully. I might be being too hard on myself though; it may be that other people are just not reacting very well to me changing my behaviour to assertive and it might be their issues rather than mine. However, I am now quite good at identifying assertive, aggressive, indirectly aggressive and passive behaviours in myself and others. This actually helps because if someone is being less than kind towards me, I can sometimes see its roots in either an aggressive or an indirectly aggressive style of behaviour. Labelling the behaviour helps, because I learned in the course that when people do use these more unpleasant behaviours, it is often because they are too scared to be assertive. As I am often too scared to be assertive, I know what that is like, so it is more understandable. The course was interesting and enjoyable and I met some new people. The course also helped me to realise I am not the only person struggling with these kinds of things. Since I do not read between the lines very much and tend to believe what people say at face value, I can very often find myself thinking that I am the only person in the world who has problems. However, it helps to remember that many other people have their problems too; they are just not talking about them and they are putting on a brave face.

Following this, I attended an alpha course at my local church, which I really enjoyed. They give you dinner, you get to chat to folk, there is a talk about an aspect of Christianity and a small group discussion time. You do not have to be a Christian to go along (most people there are not Christians) and they do not get offended if you have a different belief. It was another opportunity to meet some great people who I otherwise would never have met and to learn more about Christianity. I now attend this church most Sundays, which I would otherwise not have done.

As a child and teenager, I did a lot of dancing; ballet, tap and jazz. There was definitely a ceiling to my dancing abilities (I started off being one of the best in my class at age five due to my intelligence but as I got older, the others improved and I was often hitting the problem of not being graceful enough), but I improved a lot, and this did wonders for my balance and co-ordination. Having had a thorough dance training has made other activities such as gymnastics, trampolining, Tai Chi and many other types of dance much easier to pick up.

I have also done Ceroc Dancing. Ceroc is a very easy-to-learn jive-type dance, suitable for all ages. The men lead, the women follow, you go to a class, learn some moves, mix them up and have some nice free-style dancing too. The ceroc teaching style is very good, because they cater extremely well for beginners and they break down the steps really well and explain them thoroughly. You only learn four steps each class. Most people can dance the routine competently at the end of their first evening. Also, the ceroc community is very polite - it is extremely bad form to refuse to dance with someone and people usually change partners every dance, so it is a good confidence builder. My hand-eye co-ordination is poor, but luckily this does not affect dancing and I think many other aspies and auties would also be good at ceroc (if they do not have tactile defensiveness). And the more you do it, the better you become. Dancing is a really good mood-boost and very absorbing - if I have had a stressful day at work, by the middle of the dance class it is all forgotten. One of my friends was new in town; she started going to Ceroc and now part of her social life revolves around her dancing friends.

Joining a choir is also brilliant. I have sung with various choirs for years and participated in choir tours to Europe, the Middle East and Russia. Singing is also a brilliant antidote to a bad day at work - I think singing probably releases endorphins because it certainly makes me feel very good. Singing is also a really good way of meeting other intelligent, talented and interesting people of all ages, who otherwise might not cross your path. And although obviously not all musicians are on the spectrum, a more than average number are and a large number of the rest are either somewhere close to the spectrum or empathic enough to get along with, so it is a good place to find like-minded people.

I also did some meditation classes. Meditation really calms the mind and is especially great if you are one of these aspies/auties who, like me, is inclined to over-think things. Meditation is the mental equivalent of resting your body after exercise, in that meditation is resting your mind after being in its regular whirlwind state. Taking some classes is definitely recommended, because it helps to learn a good technique and it also helps to have regular reminders from other people about practising your meditation. I am naturally rather lazy and my mind far prefers the distraction of television to concentrating on the breath. So, although meditation is better for me, I am more tempted to watch television. Attending a class can really help motivation levels.

Tai Chi is also a good choice. I think of it as a mixture between dance and meditation. Doing Tai Chi is a quick way of calming down my mental state. The actions and balance required remind me of dance, but the calmness is similar to meditation and my body feels some of the benefits of the Alexander Technique. Tai Chi is also a good mental challenge because the routines ("forms") tend to be fairly long, taxing the memory and your copying abilities whilst you learn the forms. Trying to take in both the arm patterns and the legs at once is quite a challenge for people who monoprocess, but the slow pace of Tai Chi makes this possible. I believe that martial arts can be good for people on the spectrum too, but I have never tried this so cannot speak from personal experience.

Swimming is really great. You can explore movement in three dimensions, you get fit and aspies and auties can be very good swimmers as this is another activity which bad hand-eye co-ordination does not affect. Personally, I love swimming underwater because it is like being in a different world. It is sensory heaven. I chase bubbles made by the kicking legs of the swimmer in front and watch them rise to the surface. I swim deep along the bottom of the pool, almost flat along the bottom. I seek the flickering pattern of sunbeams at one end of the pool as the waves on the surface make the sparkly bits flicker and jump about. If I can find a hoop, I practice swimming figure of eights through and under it. And, even if the pool is crowded and confusing above the surface, it is quiet, soft and tranquil below. Swimming is also great exercise, which is very important for aspies and auties. Even if we do not like exercise, our bodies need it and I always feel much better after having been swimming. I also find swimming is very good for my digestive problems. I joined a swimming class in my local college one term and that was very handy. It was very local and joining a class meant that swimming slid easily and logically into my Wednesday routine. Perfect aspie sense.

Many people on the spectrum enjoy the creative arts. I attend a weekly art class and this is now one of my favourite things to do.

Are you eating an orange?

No-one could have been more surprised than I to discover this, however, since I have about as much drawing talent as a sheep. However, art encompasses much more than just drawing and painting. I do a lot of pottery and have started to make some prints. There are ways to get around not having any visual artistic ability. For example, I can trace over a picture instead of drawing it from scratch. With a good teacher, much can be achieved.

I also believe drama to be a very good activity; Liane Holliday Willey and various others, including one of my friends, recommend this. I have not done drama myself, but only because I was too nervous to take part; not because I did not want to. I now regret not having done this as a child when I had the opportunity. I think this would be a great activity for people on the spectrum, both in terms of being enjoyable and also as a way of learning about emotions and typical behaviour.

Another recent addition to my activities is volunteering. Volunteering always struck me as something that only very saintly people did. However, this is not true and what I never realised before is how much fun volunteering can be. I used to volunteer with a Social Group run by the National Autistic Society, where we met every month and did a different activity, such as a canal barge trip, the cinema, badminton. I went along, chatted to people and enjoyed the activity. I help out at a special needs children's club at my church. This is great because I can play cars, build lego, draw pictures of castles and interact with some brilliant and interesting kids. It has really surprised me how much I enjoy my volunteering and how important it has become to me. Singing only benefits me, but volunteering is very rewarding because I can really make a difference to someone else's life. I, and many other people on the spectrum, really do want to be helpful to other people, so volunteering is a gift in this respect. It has also been great for my self-esteem. Another good thing about volunteering is that people are often really grateful that you give your time for free and so they are patient if there are skills you still need to develop.

Autism-Friendly Activities

Another recent discovery of mine is yoga. When you feel anxious, your brain releases stress hormones as part of its "fight or flight" reaction, because the brain thinks there is some physical threat happening that needs to be fought or run away from. One of the things these stress hormones do is to tense various muscles, in preparation for the fighting or running. I feel this in my body as my calf and thigh muscles becoming tense. I am anxious quite a lot of the time, so my muscles are tense a lot. Yoga is a way of undoing this tension, with gentle exercises which encourage you to release the tension in order to be able to move further into the yoga positions. I find that releasing the tension in the muscles in turn releases the anxiety and makes my body feel brilliant afterwards.

Yoga has the further advantages of being cheap to do (join an evening class or buy a DVD) and completely non-invasive. You can do it without being touched by anyone else and you can work to your own level. I have felt put off doing yoga in the past because I am far less flexible than the average person and I do not enjoy being the worst in the class at anything. I thought that there was no point in attempting to do yoga, when even if I practised diligently every day, I would still be less flexible than the average person who did not practise at all. I usually only like to do things that I have the potential to be good at. However, I now understand it is not how far you can stretch into the positions, but the process of releasing the tension and actually doing the stretch that is important. It is not about whose body can be contorted the furthest. Also, although I cannot stretch very far, it is possible that I am benefitting more than most people from doing yoga because I need it more, as explained above. I think that many people on the spectrum could benefit from yoga.

Of course, there are many other Autism-friendly activities out there, these are just some that I have tried and enjoyed.

Tips

Have an interest in other people

Wendy Lawson (an aspie) explains that part of the recipe for successful social relationships is:

> "...the ability to 'listen' to the other person and put our own 'interest' on hold, for a while. Being listened to, heard and having one's 'needs' accommodated is the hope of every individual. Most people feel that they are not listened to and this can cause an individual to feel uncared for." (Edmonds & Beardon, 2008, p. 106).

For a long time, I was not particularly interested in other people. In conversations, it was so much effort to actually take part, that I would tend to use the gaps when others were speaking to think about what I would say next, instead of to actually listen. In my defence, being mono-channelled, thinking and listening cannot be done simultaneously. Trying to find a suitable gap in a six-pronged conversation takes the whole of my attention. However, in addition to these processing aspects, I was wrapped up in my own life and my own interests and just generally not that interested in other people.

Not being interested leads to not listening very carefully, not remembering stuff later, and this is probably often noticeable. I felt guilty for not being interested in other people, because being interested was something that nice girls "should" be, but guilt feelings do not achieve anything, so nothing changed. One day, my NT friend explained that she found other people fascinating and that she loved to people-watch on buses and in supermarket queues. She liked to guess their stories. So, I tried to adopt her attitude and I have since been much more interested in other people. To my surprise, it is quite fun. Knowing about Autism helps because I am particularly interested when I find someone with some aspie qualities. I enjoy "aspie-spotting", which requires listening, careful clue-gathering and detective work. In converse, I also enjoy noticing very un-autistic behaviours in NTs, as the contrast is sometimes huge and fascinating. Now, I am interested in other people because I want to be, rather than because I should be, and that certainly helps. This is not to say that I am now a brilliant listener, because I am often still struggling to maintain my attention on what the other person is saying. There could be an environmental distraction (such as walking and talking), or a thought might get in the way. But, I really do try.

Have a flexible attitude

We aspies/auties need our routines and structure to be able to enjoy our lives. Liane Holliday Willey (an aspie) explains that her rigid thinking and perseveration impairs communication. She cannot cope if her husband told her a sequence of time and events, and then changed his mind and altered the sequence. Even for seemingly innocuous changes, such as her husband doing the shopping before going to the bank instead of afterwards, as he had told her he would, she would be "unable to tolerate this breach in time and sequence" (Holliday Willey, 1999, p. 65).

One of my friends says that sometimes she decides not to take part in a spontaneously planned event, even though it might be an event that she really enjoys, because that event was not "supposed" to be happening that day. Even though she knows she sometimes misses out on fun things, this is what she chooses.

I believe that being flexible can save a lot of difficulty because, as they say, "if you do not bend, you break". However, I must admit that I often fail to have a flexible attitude. I am afraid this is a case of "do as I say, not as I do".

Start a conversation from the beginning and carefully link any deviation onto a new topic

Liane Holliday Willey believes aspies have seven communication problem areas, which she classifies as: brusqueness, intrusiveness, egocentrism, inappropriateness, pedantry, disjointedness and insensitivity (Holliday Willey, 2001). She explains that it is important to use appropriate transitions between topics, so that listeners can easily follow the thread of what someone is saying. The main point seems to be to link your last statement explicitly with your next statement, because although there may be a clear link in your thought processes to you, this may not be obvious to others. Liane explains this is all about realising that others cannot read minds. (In other words, this is a Theory of Mind issue.)

"During a conversation, the person with Asperger's syndrome may frequently change topics, unaware that the logical link between the topics is not obvious to the listener… The person fails to acknowledge the perspective of the listener, who is trying to follow the logic and wondering what the ultimate point will be and also whether he or she will have an opportunity to contribute to the conversation. There can be a lack of inclusive comments such as 'what do you think of that suggestion?' " (Attwood, 2007, p. 206-7).

"Luke often enters a room and, regardless of its occupants, launches into a detailed explanation of how the coding he is writing has made some spectacular change to his web page. Often he starts mid-sentence, assuming that everyone automatically knows what he is talking about - his lack of theory of mind makes this an everyday occurrence." (Jackson, 2004, p. 114).

If someone's communication style is extremely disjointed, with lots of leaps and topic shifts without warning or introduction, I can get very confused. Being aware of this, I try to make my own communication as clear as possible. However, I must admit that I sometimes trip up. An example of this was recently, which I find interesting, because I had actually read Liane Holliday Willey's books by this stage, so I was actually aware that I should try to stay on topic, and signal any deviations clearly. However, I still did not manage to do this.

I was in the lunchroom at work. The conversation was on the topic of the weather and someone mentioned wearing shorts. Now, the previous evening I had been listening to a Radio Four programme about prostitution in America and how brothels were legal in some states. I had found the programme really interesting and the mention of girls wearing shorts reminded me of it. I thought to myself, right, I had better do a graceful link here. However, there were quite a few people in this conversation and therefore I had to concentrate quite hard on finding a suitable gap into which I could speak, whilst also trying to pay attention to what other people were saying in the meantime. By the time I had found my conversation gap, I was so keen to grab it that I temporarily forgot the idea of linking my statement gracefully, and just blurted out one of the facts I had learned about prostitution in America. There was a stunned silence and then one of my friends said: "how on earth did we get onto the topic of prostitution?" and everyone started laughing at me. "Everyone" included a new French colleague, whose English was really not very good, but even she noticed that my statement was inappropriate and not linked to the conversation. So, I guess my point is, even when you know a particular rule, it is not always possible to apply it.

I would also like to point out again that I have *always* been aware that other people do not know what I am thinking. So, it was rather that I forgot to link my statement to the rest of the conversation (due to being overloaded with too many other things at that time), and not that I forgot that other people cannot read my mind. This is an example of a time when, although I might *know* a social rule, being able to use that knowledge under the pressures of real-time communication and overload, is not always possible.

Try to be aware when you might be boring someone

It is said that aspies' speech can be disorganised, tangential and egocentric (Ozonoff & Miller, 1996, cited in Martin & McDonald, 2004). Frith (1998) mentions the autistic tendency to give monologues, rather than a two-way dialogue. She says the autistic person is unlikely to change their communication, regardless of whether or not the listener shows enthusiasm.

We have probably all met at least one aspie who tends to talk in monologues, possibly about one of their special interests. If the special interest is not within my sphere of knowledge, I (and seemingly other people) may feel unable to contribute to the conversation. It might be difficult to get out of the conversation and one's attention may wander. Perhaps one reason for talking in monologues could be to control the conversation, particularly if the aspie feels stressed. Another reason could be that it may not be possible for the aspie to process normal-speed conversation (particularly in a group), so if the aspie is talking constantly, other people cannot be talking, overload is prevented, and their processing difficulties are hidden from others. I would guess that some people use this strategy on purpose, but others may be unaware they are talking in monologues. If I talk in monologues, I think it is most likely to be that I am just very interested in what I am talking about, and I may forget to take into account what will interest the other person.

However, the good news is that it is not inevitable to have this conversation style just because you are an aspie/autie. You can be aware of this tendency (if you have it) and can make an effort to switch topic after a certain length of time, or remember to ask the person you are speaking to about something that is important to them. The even better news is that some people do not mind you prattling on and on. I was on a train with my Alexander teacher recently and I had a lot to tell her, but I realised I had talked for a long time, so I mentioned this and asked her about something different. She said "well noticed" and that she did not mind because she enjoys listening to me. That was very nice and it made me feel accepted even if I do go on a bit.

The good thing about learning what social rules are, such as "do not talk too much", is that when you know the rule, you can make a conscious decision whether to keep it or break it. If you do not know the rule, you might break it unintentionally and unconsciously. In the following example, Luke (like me in many of these examples) is aware of the social rule he is breaking, but breaks it anyway.

"I am also told that I have a problem with communication because I do not know when I am boring someone. I suppose this is true. I like to talk about computers and do not usually realise that others do not want to. Well actually I do, but when I am thinking about computers I am not thinking about anyone else." (Jackson, 2002b, p. 22).

For myself, I am sometimes unaware when I am boring someone. I still find that my conversations with people tend to be one-sided. If I phone someone, I try to remember to ask how they are and to remember their last piece of important news, but after that I will prattle on and on and on and on and on about the fascinating things in my life for far too long. I feel guilty about this, but it is partly because lots of interesting things do happen to me that I want to talk about, and I get carried away. However, I hereby resolve to stop feeling guilty, because guilt is pointless and does not help anyone.

I think a friend of a friend may be an aspie. When I met him recently, in a conversation, he was effectively holding a lecture on a particular topic. He kept interjecting his lecture with comments like "I am probably boring you". I thought it was a pity, because what he was saying was very interesting. I think this shows that he has to say this, because he is aware that he will not pick up such vibes by instinct. However, it comes across as very negative (self-deprecating) to pepper your speech with this phrase all the time. So, there does not seem to be an easy solution to this issue. Perhaps the best thing is to tell people to be very blunt if you are, in fact, boring them too much, so that you then know when to stop, before they become really irritated and decide that you are too arrogant to spend time with.

So, if you have a tendency to prattle on like I do, just try to be aware of it now and again and temper your speech with some questions to allow the other person to contribute. Do not beat yourself up about it though, because it is just one of your many lovable characteristics.

Avoid being too honest

Let's start with some aspie/autie views on honesty:

"Sometimes I consider Asperger Syndrome to be 'the honesty disease' as Aspergics are often totally frank and honest... sometimes brutally so. Having a lack of emotional understanding, it is very difficult to grasp how a piece of information or an action will be received or interpreted. The concept of 'sugar-coating' just doesn't ever occur. This isn't down to Aspergic people being cruel or deliberately nasty but comes back to not understanding or realizing that an action will result in a particular response/reaction." Neil Shepherd, writing in Edmonds & Beardon (2008, p. 53).

Kenneth Hall describes honesty as "maybe the very best part [of AS]" (Hall, 2001, p. 65).

Given that many NTs happily teach their children "honesty is the best policy", the effects of actually being honest are rather surprising to me. Luke Jackson's Mum explains:

"Whilst I see Luke as enchantingly candid, his honesty being a refreshing well of clear water in a world that is too often filled with grimy duplicity, the rest of the family sometimes don't see it in quite the same way. The girls don't take kindly to being told their backsides look big, their make-up stupid or their boyfriends being told that they are the third one that week!" (Jackson, 2004, p. 114).

I have learned that honesty is not always received very well and that some people only seem to want to listen to what I have to say if I can express myself in an "acceptable" way, whatever that means. This causes a lot of stress, because I am not very good at guessing what other people would deem acceptable. In such cases, I tend to stop communicating. This does not always work though, because I can get into real difficulties but still not communicate, and then I get asked why did I not say something about it before. What matters to me is the underlying message that I am communicating, or that others are communicating to me, and it does not occur to me to spend valuable time and effort fussing with the frills on the message by deciding exactly how to say it. I am pretty sure I would not be any good at arranging the frills anyway, even if it did occur to me to try. It seems to me that the autistic world judges what you say, but the NT world judges how you say it. This really sucks, but that is life.

Avoid too much self-disclosure

Many aspies and auties are self-disclosers. For example, Liane Holliday Willey writes:

"It was easy for me to give my opinions on things, virtually all the time. I was by far the most blunt and outspoken of our group, even when my friends suggested I had gone too far. I never knew how far was too far. Even now, I cannot find one reliable reason for keeping my thoughts to myself. The world seems fickle on this point. Sometimes people want an opinion, sometimes they do not... The entire dichotomy is too confusing. I do not see how anyone can even know with any degree of certainty when they should voice their thoughts and when they should keep them silent... Sometimes I even wish I had not said what I did. But I realised long ago that it would be easier for me to stop a dog from going after a bone, than it would be for me to stop my thoughts from escaping my mouth." (Holliday Willey, 1999, p. 28).

Cornish also knows about this issue:

"Personal disclosure. NTs are so used to making sure that no-one gets any personal information on them, and put simply, they cannot trust each other not to use it to hurt each other. It is something they expect of one another. How many times has it been said that Aspergians are too trusting? For a lot of us, we simply don't suspect that there's anything to suspect! This makes it very difficult for someone like an Aspergian, who doesn't naturally have an agenda to gain superiority over others, to feel safe in a very dodgy world. And make no mistake, the main NT agenda, given the chance, is superiority over inferiority." (Edmonds & Beardon, 2008, p. 155).

I also tend towards too much self-disclosure. If something is interesting me or bothering me, I tend to talk about it, sometimes with my colleagues at work. My friend has explained to me that most people do not do this; they instead stick to insignificant topics like the weather or popular movies. Self-disclosure can have its good points. I frequently find myself making other people laugh by my stories. Stuff just happens to me that would not happen to anyone else. Sometimes, other people laugh when I am being completely serious, and that is fine with me too, because they are almost always laughing in a friendly way (I can tell the difference between affectionate mocking and malice). Furthermore, one colleague said that if it were not for me and one other person, lunchtimes would be boring, which is a very nice compliment.

However, one downside is that occasionally, I find someone who laughs at me in a very mean way. Possibly another downside is that I show myself to be weird or eccentric, which should not actually be a bad thing, but actually in NT society, it probably is. I am not usually aware of the direct consequences of this. Another downside of too much self-disclosure is the fact that others do not do this, and therefore can misinterpret my feelings about what I am talking about. Remember my story in the chapter on Faux Pas about saying to my flatmate that her friend's nose was shaped like a ski-slope? Well, I was very upset about this and when I am upset about something, I tell people about it, hoping to end up feeling better. Therefore, the next lunchtime, I told this story at work, because I hoped my friends/colleagues would help me to process it and get over it. However, instead, I found that people laughed and teased me about it, which I was not comfortable with, because I was feeling very guilty about the whole incident and too sore about it to find it amusing. I am fine with people laughing at me for many things, but I was not fine about that. When I asked one of my friends, in private, to stop teasing me for that particular incident, he responded that he thought teasing me would teach me to be more considerate next time. That was a magnificent result of someone not realising I am autistic, as it was not a matter of me becoming more considerate. I simply needed to learn yet another social rule (do not say anything specific about someone's appearance even if you do not think they look ugly) that I had not yet learned. This was the failure, rather than a lack of consideration.

My friend explained to me later, that if you tell a story like that in a public setting, people assume that you are completely okay with the story and that it is "fair game" to tease you about it. Other people would assume that if I was not okay with being teased about it, I would not have placed the story in the public arena. So, they were not intentionally being nasty, but they would not have understood that this was something I felt badly about and did not want to be teased about. My friend also explained that other people would therefore keep personal issues very close to their chest and only discuss trivialities in public. It sounds very much like a game of poker to me, with each person playing tactically to improve their social position. She explained that if I give something away, like an interesting bit of information, other people can capitalise on that, without incurring any risk to their own social standing. This ties in a lot with what Cornish said above.

Bizarrely, the downside of potentially attracting bullying/mean comments can also be considered an upside. If there are nasty people in my environment, they may well pick on me as an easy target. So, without any kind of intuitive mind-reading skill, I can sometimes tell you who is a nice person and who is not. Jacqui Jackson also shares this view. She explains how her younger two autistic spectrum boys are used by their sisters as a good way to judge the character of others, "like a canary in a mine" (Jackson, 2004, p. 162). When they bring a new friend or potential boyfriend into the house, if the person recoils in disgust or anger, they are dismissed, but if they accept the boys, then they are deemed suitable. Completely coincidentally, I have also thought of myself as a mine canary for a slightly different reason. If the environment is bad in some way, because my stress levels tend to be higher than other people's to start with (having to deal with all of these issues will do that), I am usually the first to fall off my perch.

Have a lot of stamina and be prepared for exhaustion

"Many of them [children with AS] make some attempt at pretending to be 'normal' and however successful an AS person appears to be, wearing a mask comes at a cost. To run an 'emulator' is immensely tiring" (Jackson, 2004, p. 117).

One of Tony Attwood's clients describes her exhaustion from socialising by saying "I am all peopled out" (Attwood, 2007, p. 123).

I cannot add very much to this, except to agree, wholeheartedly. Coping with social interaction in a work environment where I need to understand complex information in a short time and where accuracy is crucial, often leaves me exhausted. When I worked full time, by the time five o'clock came, I was sometimes not capable of firing two neurons together.

My friend has a good explanation of the exhaustion. She says aspies have to run at 100% effort all the time to achieve 60% of what the world expects. Auties also run at 100% effort and achieve 30% of what the world expects. Therefore, being an aspie is not "mild Autism" because both groups are running at 100% effort. So, if you are tired out, that is not surprising and you are not a wimp. Give yourself a pat on the back and be kind to yourself.

Try to learn the rules

Very importantly, learning the rules does *not* mean that you must follow them. For example, I rather enjoying breaking a few social rules as I go along. I do not have a particularly conforming nature, so when I think that my own way is more sensible, I tend to follow it.

However, it is logical to try to know the rules and to be aware of the consequences of breaking them. This means that you can be a conscious rule-breaker (if you wish to), rather than unconsciously getting yourself into trouble that could have been avoided. Knowing the rules gives you the power to decide whether to follow them or not.

Appreciate that you are very courageous

Since us autistic folk will probably not get our communication quite "right" in the world's opinion, and since most of us have a ton of bad communication experiences behind us, we need a massive amount of courage to interact in the knowledge of this. For some people, even stepping outside the security of their home requires heroism:

Are you eating an orange?

"It is terribly difficult to believe in one's self-worth if one has been criticised, ridiculed, bullied or left out for years on end" (Liane Holliday Willey, writing in Edmonds & Beardon, 2008, p. 120).

"...so much effort goes into controlling the fear and 'pain' (or rather hiding the fear and pain) that you don't actually have enough processing power left to hold the conversation, understand what's being said or form rational responses" (Neil Shepherd, writing in Edmonds & Beardon, 2008, p. 58).

Amen to that.

Courage is doing something that you are afraid of. If other people are not afraid, they do not need courage. A friend of mine who had led a group of us on a walking trip was telling me afterwards how much he admired me, because I had been terrified on one particular expedition (it was a particularly difficult winter climb of a snowy, stormy mountain) but I had done it anyway. Near the top of the mountain, the top covering of snow and ice was getting blown into our faces like an onslaught of needles and the wind was so strong that we were getting blown off our feet. I was quite surprised that he said that, because the rest of our group had coped much better than I did. But he said that he admired me because I was terrified of it, whereas the others were not.

So, if you find yourself chastising yourself for being too timid, or for wimping out of something that others can do quite easily, go easy on yourself. The rest of the world may not understand what things require particular heroism for you to carry them out. You might actually be a whole lot braver than you think.

Combating the Effects of Over-Thinking

Aspies and auties think a lot. We have to. We have to work much harder than NTs do, to figure out what we should do and say and what society's norms are. Whilst NTs can do this fairly effortlessly, for us, it takes considerable mental effort. Even beyond this, as hopefully you can understand from the chapters on sensory issues, we are having to work harder than other people with information processing, which gives a bit of an autistic delay into our whole lives. I sometimes feel like I am operating with a three second delay compared to other people. Actually, our brains are churning round on over-drive most of the time. This is a very sensible and useful thing – just think what would happen if we gave up trying to figure anything out because it was just too difficult – we would be nothing more than compliant and agreeable vegetables. However, this constant over-drive thinking is exhausting and stressful. It also leads to the problem of not being able to switch off the thinking channel and relax. Being mono-channelled, the more time we spend in the thinking channel, the less time we have in any of the sensory input channels, and therefore the less we know about the world around us.

The effects of over-thinking on sleep

I believe many folk on the spectrum suffer from insomnia. In some cases, it may be a biological thing – the sleep clock is just not set correctly in the person's head. I am not sure what can be done about this, because the body clock needs to be reset. I have a friend who effectively has jet-lag twice a year when the clocks move forward and back, because although the time moves, his sleep clock does not. Try to have a regular bedtime, a regular waking up time and a nice comforting bedtime routine.

In my case, I do not think I have sleep clock resetting problems, but I have had lots of problems getting off to sleep. This problem seems to be caused by not being able to stop thinking, and thinking keeps me awake. I hit upon a solution to this as a teenager. I listen to story CDs. What I usually choose are instalments of Harry Potter or thirty-minute comedies such as Blackadder, Yes Minister, Navy Lark, but what you choose does not really matter. I reasoned with myself that:

1)   if I fall asleep, I win because I am trying to fall asleep.
2)   if I do not fall asleep, I will at least enjoy a nice story, and so I also win by having a nice time.

Hence, it is a win-win situation and, secure in this knowledge, I usually fall asleep within the first five minutes! Do not worry if you think the comedy will keep you laughing so much that you will not fall asleep – I can pretty much recite all my CDs by heart now, and when you have heard them so many times, they do not keep you awake. I think this technique works for me, because listening to a story tape switches my hearing channel on and therefore my thinking channel gets switched off, as I am a mono-channelled person. Hence, thinking can no longer keep me awake and I doze off.

A second thing that really helped my sleep problems was doing a stint as a night-shift worker. Okay, this is probably not practical for most readers, but I took a temporary job where I was working 10:30pm to 10:30am for four nights in a row and then I had four days off. I found sleeping in the daytime was quite difficult (an eye mask helped), but I was so tired from the twelve hour shift that I did manage it. After this job finished, I found that I was now so well-trained in sleeping at odd hours, that sleeping at night suddenly became a doddle. I found this a surprising effect of having had a night-shift job, but it has really helped.

Self-esteem

On an assertiveness course I did a few years ago, I learned that an amazing percentage of our thoughts are repetitive ones. It is something like 85%-95%. The thoughts of aspies and auties can be confused and over-loaded, for example, in trying to understand a social situation that has gone wrong. Our lives are more difficult than normal lives and may not be so strewn with the successes that seem to come so easily to other folk. Combining these kinds of thoughts with more than the average quantity of thoughts, and adding in an 85% repeat factor, you can see how easy it is to get stuck in negative thinking.

If you are on the spectrum, you will be spending a considerable amount of time thinking, as explained above. If you have high self-esteem, your repetitive thoughts will be pleasant. If you have low self-esteem, they will be unpleasant. Therefore, it makes sense to do whatever you can to increase your self-esteem.

Negative thinking has been a big problem for me for most of my life. I like to find happy, successful people and try to figure out how they do it, by asking them for their opinions on various things. Here are a few helpful philosophies that I have picked up:

1.   "Always remember, different is cool." Luke Jackson, aspie.

This is a really important one. Different does not mean defective. Different means interesting.

2.   "Normal is not what it is cracked up to be. You would not want to be normal anyway." Dawn Menzies, friend.

I did not believe this one the first time I heard it. I *did* want to be normal. However, it is really important to get yourself believing this. I am pretty much there now. I have a friend who has a high-level spinal injury and a high level of support needs. However, he has a brilliant life that he is in control of; he goes out and does lots of cool stuff like jumping out of planes and scuba diving. He told me that if there were a pill that could make him walk again, he would not take it, because being disabled has been such a big part of his life for so long and has permeated every aspect of his life and his decisions. He definitely believes that he would not take such a pill. In a way, you are sunk if you do not. Life cannot be any different, either for me or my friend. He cannot walk and I cannot stop being an aspie, even if I wanted to. To spend your life wishing for the impossible to happen is not a good idea.

3.   "It does not matter if you succeed or fail. All you have to be concerned about is that you try your best." David Hall, cousin.

This is true. If you tried your best, you can hold your head up high. It is all any of us can do.

4.   "It is okay to make mistakes." Personal development book.

I struggle with this one, as I tend to be too much of a perfectionist. But it is a very valuable piece of your armoury. No-one is perfect, this includes you, and that is okay.

5.   "The opinions that most people have about you, do not matter. It only matters what the people who care about you think." Jamie Allan, friend.

Fundamentally, it does not matter what your colleagues think or people with whom you only have a casual acquaintance. The opinions of the world in general do not affect your identity. After all, no-one can please everyone, all of the time.

6.   "No-one is better than you. No-one is worse than you." Sinead Feeney, friend.

Do not compare yourself to other people. This is a short-cut to unhappiness, whether you are comparing yourself as better or worse off to the other person in question. If you go around thinking you are better than other people, you become proud and not nice to be around. If you go around thinking you are worse than other people, your self-esteem takes a hit and you feel bad.

Of course, these are just a few good philosophies to get you started; it is not an exhaustive list. I am sure you can come up with many more.

Needs

In this chapter, I am going to discuss some of my needs as an autistic person.

People on the autistic spectrum tend to understand and use language in a very literal manner (Welton, 2004, cited in Humphrey, 2008) and therefore any non-literal language can be problematic. When other people get annoyed with me, it is usually caused by my understanding and speech being very literal, unlike theirs. I have listed some of my needs below. The first two needs are related to these issues.

1.   Clear and concrete directions

If people communicate to me in an indirect way, it is likely that I will miss the main point of the message, even if I understand the literal words (see the examples in the chapters on Communication and Social Mishap Stories). Indirect communication is particularly problematic for me because I will probably not realise that I have missed the main message, because of understanding the literal meaning. In such cases, I cannot ask for clarification because I am not aware that anything is unclear. Failure to understand indirect communication can lead other people to come to the wrong conclusion about me.

As a consequence of my literal understanding, I need people to be very clear and precise, to say exactly what they mean and tell me exactly what to do. This need also results from the difficulties I, and other spectrum folk, have in generalising from one situation to another (Holliday Willey, 2001).

2.   People to understand my literal communication

The problems with indirect speech cut both ways; it causes problems both when I am receiving and when I am communicating speech. I am not sure whether most people realise this, because they might be tempted to think it would be just a problem when I am the receiver.

If someone asks me a question and I respond by telling them something they already know, they may take offence if they think I am insulting their intelligence. However, I may tell them something they already know because I am not aware of what they know, because I do not see any other possible response and I am just trying to answer the question, and/or because I do not have time to consider what they do already know under the pressure of real-time communication, without a long time to ponder what exactly they could be asking. For example, the statement from a colleague: "you will have to tell me what to do with this invoice" resulted in me explaining exactly how to make up an invoice (to answer the question), but the meaning was: "I do not know what narrative to put in the invoice and I would like you to tell me what narrative to put".

I think the cause of this difficulty is that some people might assume that, like most people, I also communicate indirectly, with implications and hints. So, when I make a statement, people can read far more into it than what I say and mean. Actually, my statements are just statements. Once, I said to a colleague: "this file does not match this letter", and they were furious at me. I actually meant nothing more than this simple fact. In particular, I did not mean: "this file does not match this letter so I think you are stupid and lazy and incapable for having made this awful mistake". If I had wanted to say that (which I did not), I would have said that explicitly.

Part of the problem could have been if my face was doing something that I was not aware of at the time when I made that statement. I remember someone telling me once that my face looked like thunder, when I was not angry at anything at the time, just thinking. I was really surprised to learn that I could appear angry when I am not. So, if I am frowning, it might just be that I am concentrating and it does not necessarily mean that I am angry. However, since I am not aware of what my face looks like and since I do not have a stored repertoire of what faces "should" look like at all times, I cannot do anything about it. I am also having to think so hard all the time anyway, that even if I had such face-organisational abilities, I would not have any spare processing time in which I could use them. And I hardly think going round with a permanently silly grin at all times, just in case I accidentally might look angry, would help matters.

So, I need people to be patient, understanding, to listen, to not fly off the handle and to see the real reasons behind what I say and do. I need people not to be offended when I tell them things they already know. Some people are great about this. I used to tell one former colleague something he already knew on a regular basis. He would laugh at me in a kind way and tell me that he knew it. He was not upset, I was not upset, and I could then get on and tell him something he did not already know.

What happens when needs 1 and 2 are not met

When people do become annoyed at me, this always comes out of the blue and as a complete shock, as I am trying to be nice. As I am not trying to cause it, I am not expecting it and can never be mentally prepared for the next time it will happen. The result is that I can get into a permanent state of high anxiety, because there is always a chance that I will receive an angry reception on any instance of interaction. Anxiety "disorder"? I do not think so, it seems perfectly reasonable to be anxious to me.

Each time, I struggle to understand why the person is annoyed - the interaction is usually over long before I know why they are upset, and even then, I do not know how to put the situation right. I have tried asking other people for advice, but as they cannot give a list of rules or predict every possibility, this does not actually help very much. Sometimes, disclosing my aspie-status helps. But some people do not believe me when I tell them ("you are too intelligent", "that is an excuse", "you are a hypochondriac", "only children are autistic"). Other people may believe me but not understand the implications, even after many times of trying to explain it to them.

Despite a few attempts on my part to explain Autism to one of my previous bosses, he seemed to find it hard to understand the implications for everyday situations. One example is me trying to explain to him that I could not concentrate on my work when someone nearby was talking on the telephone. My boss immediately responded that "professionals do *not* get disturbed by noise". Thus, our ensuing discussion centred on whether or not I was having the problem whereas, in my opinion, a more helpful approach would have been to try to solve the problem. At the end of our discussion, I still had not managed to convince my boss that the problem existed.

For my part, I got side-tracked into this discussion about whether or not I was having the problem, which took up all my processing abilities. Due to this overwhelm and my lack of Theory of Non-Autistic Mind, I did not realise at the time that I was not making the best possible argument to convince my boss that I was not just making a fuss about nothing.

I did not manage to realise that I needed to explain from first principles why I was having that particular problem. Instead of just saying that I could not work when someone nearby was talking on the telephone, I should have argued the following points:

1.   I have AS.
2.   I have sensory processing difficulties.
3.   I only process one channel at once.
4.   I cannot think and listen at the same time.
5.   Listening precedes thinking in my brain's precedent list when it comes to human speech within earshot.

6.   I cannot think when someone within earshot is speaking on the telephone.
7.   I cannot do my work when this is happening.

I knew all of these facts at that time, so I had all the information that I needed to ensure my boss understood that I was not just being a fuss-pot, but I did not realise what part of my knowledge I needed to explicitly say. Being an honest person, I just assumed my boss would believe me when I said the problem existed and I did not realise he would need to know exactly why the problem was there in order to believe me. He did not ask the right questions (and I think he leapt to judgement too quickly by telling me the problem did not exist) and I did not provide the necessary information. In this situation, I think my boss was displaying a lack of Theory of Autistic Mind, just as I was displaying a lack of Theory of Non-Autistic Mind!

My natural expectation for such situations is that because I am honest, people who know me should realise that I am honest, and therefore I should be believed. However, I have learned from this that in reality, to be believed, if I am dealing with a situation that is affected by Autism in any way, then I have to give full detailed support for any statements I make. I have to particularly remember that NTs are not sharing my viewpoint, and also that NTs might not realise that I am honest and/or that my sensitivity to my environment is real and not made-up.

3.   People to believe what I tell them!

I am a very honest person; I find lying repellent in most circumstances and I am awful at it. Given this, I find it bizarre, and very frustrating, that so many people disbelieve what I tell them.

Some people do not believe that I am on the autistic spectrum and therefore refuse to consider this as a mitigating factor if we have any misunderstandings. My friend did not believe me when I told him I cannot understand body language. No-one believes me if I say I cannot multi-task: "but you're a girl…" People do not believe me when I tell them how great the Alexander Technique is; they instead mock me for doing it. And common responses to me saying I am autistic are: "no, you are very sociable, you are deluded"; "no, watch out, or it will become a self-fulfilling prophecy, stop thinking about it". This makes me want to scream and sometimes I feel that any attempt at communication is hopeless.

4.   Honesty and follow-through from others

Tony Attwood (2007) says that aspies have a greater allegiance to the truth than to the thoughts/feelings of others. I get very upset if anyone does anything that seems unethical to me. On such occasions, I have sometimes protested, but usually all this achieves is to get me into trouble, whilst not changing the situation. This is an example of me being on the side of truth, whilst bringing myself into conflict with others. If this goes on for a while, I may stop protesting, try not to think about it and learn to shut up, which is better for my personal survival. I tend to have boundary issues in which I feel a moral responsibility in situations that are completely out of my hands, where all the decisions and power actually lie with someone else. I can feel guilty for situations that are nothing to do with me. I will try in future to discriminate between situations that are "my stuff" and those that are not.

Likewise, if someone says "I'll phone you back later today/next week/after my exam", I believe that they will and I get upset if they do not. To me, that feels like lying. I start wondering if they do not like me enough to bother to keep their word. I am not sure about when I should contact them again, because the absence of communication makes it unclear. Other people have explained that when people say "I'll phone you back after lunch", they do have a genuine intention to do it at the time but then they just forget. I think that if people say they are going to do something, they should do it. I try to keep my word to other people.

5.   To know other people like me

One of the best things about discovering my aspie-ness is meeting other aspies/auties. Their company is quite relaxing, as they operate at a similar speed to me and tend to have similar values. They have things in common with me; they do what they say they will; they understand the frustrations of life on the spectrum; they care about animals; they are fair-minded; they may have some very funny stories; they do not want to meet me in a crowded pub/night club; and if they are going to say something, they say it explicitly and do not try to communicate with me by wiggling their left eyebrow!

Also, if we are in an Autism training session and I am trying to explain myself to NTs, it is sometimes a struggle to get even the professionals to understand something that is outside of their experience. There is something very nice about having someone else on the spectrum there, who will understand and who can back me up. It is much better than being a minority of one. Liane Holliday Willey agrees:

"...few things make me happier than the moments I discover another aspie in our midst... Nothing lights up the aspie face like the realisation they are spending time with a fellow thinker." (Holliday Willey, 2001, p. 27).

Dominique Dumortier also feels the same way; on first meeting other autistic people, she said: "for the first time in my life I felt at home" (Dumortier, 2002).

Fortunately, autistic people do seem to magnetically attract each other. At one social event I attended, people naturally split off into smaller groups to walk to the pub and I found myself in the company of two aspies (who do not know they are aspies). Remarkable.

6.   Solitude

I can get over-loaded if I have too much social interaction. I think this is because I need to think quite hard in social situations and certainly more than most NTs. I remember saying to my friend that I was not going to go to a particular party because I was tired and did not have the mental energy for it. She responded by telling me that attending a party did not require any mental energy. Which, for her, I am sure it did not. Therefore, whilst others might find socialising purely relaxing, I think I find it more strenuous than most. It seems that NTs "recharge themselves" by socialising. In contrast, for me to recharge requires solitude. If I do not get enough solitude, I become mentally exhausted and possibly grumpy.

The length of time one is supposed to spend in the presence of another person and the lack of solitude is one of my main problems when it comes to relationships. Society says that people "in love" should want to be with each other a lot of the time. However, I am usually very thankful when my date goes home and I get some much needed peace. This causes me to think that I cannot be "in love" because I am not feeling how society tells me that "in love" feels. I wonder if there is another way…? I think there must be because many people on the spectrum have very successful relationships. However, I am yet to experience this.

7.   For other people to accept me as I am

When other people are misunderstanding me and leaping to conclusions about my communication, when they are trying to mould me into something I am not, and when they are full of condemnation when I do not live up to exacting NT standards of behaviour, it is easy to feel that I am a bad and unworthy person.

I may not need a special Autism-related service to manage my life in great detail, but I do need a supportive and understanding environment in which to live, work and play.

People vary hugely in their reactions to me. For every person who finds my differences too intimidating because I am alien to their nature, there will be another who thinks different is cool, will be interested and will make the effort to get to know me.

I am pretty lucky to have some truly great and supportive people in my life - some from the Autism world, from my time at University, from my church and at my work, and that can make an enormous difference. I really like it when I talk to someone who does "get me". Then I know I am not alone.

If other people already accept me, then it is much, much easier to accept myself, the final "need":

8.   To accept myself

Liane Holliday Willey has a self-affirmation pledge for aspies and the last point of this is "I will accept myself for who I am". Self-acceptance can be difficult for me and other aspies/auties. We have to work hard at many things that come naturally to NTs. We have to consciously do many things that NTs do intuitively, without thinking. And whilst we are logically working things out, one channel at a time, other people are skipping along ahead of us and we can feel slow and stupid. We are obvious targets for the not-so-nice elements in society. And even the nice ones can, through continued misunderstanding, contribute to a lot of stress. It is hard to keep high self-esteem whilst receiving continual knock-backs.

Having people misunderstand me frequently makes me feel lonely; not physically, but mentally. Work is harder, friendships are harder, relationships are harder, keeping my head above water is harder. A natural response when life is a constant struggle,when I am trying my best but getting continual negative feedback, is to believe that I am undeserving.

Needs

A few years ago, I felt pretty bad about myself, but now, things are much better. I know that the difficulties I have are not all caused by me, but partly by others, and I know that it is not my fault if I am wired-up differently to other folk. I am collecting and adding nice people to my life all the time, as well as discovering an ever-increasing number of aspies/auties, both newly collected, or new discoveries from old, like-minded acquaintances. Since no bully or genuinely nasty person would wish to be my friend, I find myself surrounded by top quality people.

A lot of minority groups have the aim of assimilation into the majority culture. People from abroad come to Britain and try to fit into British culture; they learn the language, they get jobs, they try to fit in with society the best they can. Women try to fit into the male-dominated business world by wearing suits and adopting male attitudes. If you are deaf, you can learn to lip read so you can communicate with people who do not know sign language. If you are physically disabled, you can carry your own mini-ramp in your car to accommodate a lack of wheelchair ramps. Aspies/auties can try to fit into the NT world by pretending to be normal. To a certain extent, this pretending has to be done, if you want an easier life. But too much pretending involves an overwhelming effort to make yourself acceptable to NTs and in so doing, there is a constant pressure that you, just as you are, are not acceptable. Thus, you are in danger of losing your soul, or never finding it in the first place.

I am proud to be an aspie and I do not want to be cured of being myself. I would like a more tolerant and less judgmental society, so that I no longer have to pretend so hard to be normal. I will never be a very good NT-imitation; instead I want to be the best aspie I can be.

Acceptance

In my opinion, the best thing to do with a diagnosis of Autism is to accept it and learn to be happy about it. It is quite possible to see Autism as a gift not a curse; as a different culture rather than a disability. If you do not accept your diagnosis and spend your whole life denying it and trying to fit into the mainstream, you might be unhappy but without the information and the tools to help you sort yourself out. The goal is that you need to be pleased to be you, whatever that means, with all your traits, imperfections, quirks, talents and disadvantages.

One nice thing about Autism is it brings so many good qualities with the negative ones. For every "symptom" as the doctors like to say, there is a way to turn it into a nice thing. For example, I do tend to lose the big picture, but I have got a great eye for detail. It is a good thing to believe that if there were a pill that could magically stop you from being autistic, you would not take it. Otherwise, you may well be miserable. No-one should spend their life wishing they were someone else.

One thing that can make acceptance difficult is, although some people might have a positive view about Autism, not everyone in the world shares this view. One of my friends was initially very concerned when she learned about my diagnosis and asked me why I did not want to "fight it". She seemed to think I should refuse the label. But this does not seem logical to me, because even if I refuse to accept the label "autistic", that does not alter the fact that I am autistic. You cannot "fight Autism" in the same way as you might fight an infectious disease. It is about having a differently wired brain and there is no possible brain transplant because a different brain means a different person. If I did choose to deny Autism, I would still have the same personality and the same issues; I would just be much more ignorant about myself. I wish people could see that it just means belonging to a different culture, just as someone who is French comes from a different culture. If the general public understood that being autistic was just a different culture, they might not get so freaked out about it, and autistic people might find it easier to accept their diagnosis, or to seek out a diagnosis if they suspect it in themselves.

I guess a negative attitude to Autism is pretty common, but all this seems to be doing is persuading lots of aspies that it is better to deny Autism and remain undiagnosed. It is a self-perpetuating problem because it means that the majority of people who end up being diagnosed are the lower-functioning ones or the ones who are in a really bad way and need the diagnosis to access services. This serves to maintain stereotypes such as intelligent, social people cannot possibly be autistic. The very highest-functioning aspies without major problems deny Autism to protect their self-image and their image in our society, perpetuating the myth that all Autism is very severe and high-functioning people like me do not in fact exist.

Considering Autism as a different culture, there is always a much higher risk of communication failure when two different cultures interact. Countless wars have occurred between different cultures at different times in our history. I have noticed that in University and work situations, people from the same country seem to stick together. And you only have to watch "Fawlty Towers" (a TV situation comedy) to see some of the communication problems between the English owner of Fawlty Towers and his Spanish waiter.

However, just as actually being from a different country brings a different culture, so does being on the spectrum. NTs and spectrum folk operate at different speeds; spectrum folk tend to be slower at processing. They are interested in different things. A hypothetical NT may like: fashion, celebrity culture, small talk, spontaneity, loud pubs and flashy cars. A hypothetical spectrum person may like: talking as a means to exchange information, one-to-one social situations/small groups, quiet places, cycling, routines and time to oneself. Furthermore, our NT may value conforming to be the same as everyone else, outward appearances, the ability to deceive, shrewdness and popularity. Our spectrum person may value honesty, integrity, diligence, loyalty, originality and individuality. Of course, I do not think all NTs are alike, any more than all spectrum people, but I do believe these illustrate some core differences.

Do you not think this is a different culture?

Once you accept that Autism is a different culture, you can help yourself by studying NT culture, like an anthropologist. And you are in luck, there is a lot of it about! NT culture is everywhere you look… So, you have many more opportunities to study NT culture than NTs have to study autistic culture.

My example "Are you eating an orange?" mentioned earlier, taught me about one cultural difference between people on the spectrum and NTs. I learned that some people think it is rude to be direct by saying "I think you should not eat an orange on public transport", whilst thinking it is polite to be indirect, by asking "Are you eating an orange?" whilst intending to imply that this behaviour is inappropriate. Thus, when it comes to rudeness, NTs apparently think that the thing to be judged is the offensiveness of their indirect, coded message, taken only at face value and not interpreted, even though there is an assumption that the message *will* be interpreted.

This does not make sense to me. If you are sure that your indirect code will be interpreted, why is only the rudeness of the coded version judged, and the rudeness of the uncoded version ignored? I think that people should be judged on their intended meaning, rather than how this intended meaning is expressed. Therefore, in the matter of rudeness, I do not find one of the above expressions more offensive than the other. I only find one expression more confusing than the other.

Acceptance

Coming from two such different cultures is likely to make cross-cultural communication between NTs and aspies/auties difficult. If you are talking to someone from Spain, you are instantly aware that you are speaking to someone from a different culture and you can make allowances and adapt your communication. However, in the case of spectrum-NT communications, the NT is often not even aware that they are speaking to an aspie/autie (and hence is not even aware of the existence of the cultural difference). Even if they *are* aware, they often do not understand how to adapt. Also, since many adult aspies and auties are not diagnosed, in many cases, the person on the spectrum is not aware of their cultural difference either.

It is interesting that many people on the spectrum (myself included) often get along better with people from a foreign country. For example, I have always got on best with flatmates from foreign countries. In this case, both parties are aware they are speaking with someone from another culture and they make allowances for the other. Also, any slight weirdnesses of the aspie/autie are more likely to be interpreted as foreign differences rather than actual weirdnesses. A foreign person, not using their mother-tongue, has very similar issues to people on the spectrum. Their communication might be slower and less fluent. They might not know all of the social references in conversations (such as which soap stars were famous in the UK in 1990). They might have difficulty communicating with people who have strong regional accents. Their "foreign delay" is similar to my "autistic delay" in many ways and contributes to us operating at a similar speed. To my amusement, my last foreign flatmate was far better than me at adopting the local slang. For example, I would say to a bus driver in my posh accent: "I would like to go to XX please"; whereas my flatmate taught me to say the much more normal: "90p please".

Since people on the spectrum and foreign people are able to get on so well, this supports the view that if society in general was more educated about Autism and the cultural differences it brings, there is no reason why NTs and people on the spectrum cannot live harmoniously side-by-side.

For balance, I would like to clarify that I do not find communicating with every NT to be difficult. With some NTs, communication is very easy and they seem to understand where I am coming from and know the right way to explain things to me, even without knowing anything about Autism. However, unfortunately, these bright lights in my life tend to be few and far between.

Conclusion

One of my aims in writing this book is to tell you that Autism is not a big, scary horrible thing that has to be run away from, and if you embrace it, you are likely to feel better in the long run. I also wish to help educate society to embrace Autism as well, so that the barriers/prejudices that society puts up against Autism get taken down. As evidence of the existence of these barriers, there is the attitude quite a few people had towards me; they spotted that I was on the spectrum before I was diagnosed, but did not tell me about it because they feared I would be offended/hurt/insulted. If society as a whole views Autism as an insult and a tragedy, this is just making it harder for us to accept ourselves. If, in writing this book, I have informed and entertained you and hopefully made you feel better about Autism, I will consider this a job well done.

When I read what some other people write/teach about Autism, it can be so negative, and I sometimes wish people could see how cool we are. We are not inferior versions of NTs, who desperately wish to become NTs! I would like to give the last word to Muskie, an autistic person, who perhaps was thinking along similar lines, when he wrote his definition of Neurotypical Syndrome. Perhaps all NTs should read this, especially before teaching/training in the field of Autism. I find it a good antidote to too much talk about my "impairments":

What is NT?

"Neurotypical syndrome is a neurobiological disorder characterized by preoccupation with social concerns, delusions of superiority, and obsession with conformity. Neurotypical individuals often assume that their experience of the world is either the only one, or the only correct one. NTs find it difficult to be alone. NTs are often intolerant of seemingly minor differences in others. When in groups NTs are socially and behaviourally rigid, and frequently insist upon the performance of dysfunctional,

231

destructive, and even impossible rituals as a way of maintaining group identity. NTs find it difficult to communicate directly, and have a much higher incidence of lying as compared to persons on the autistic spectrum. NT is believed to be genetic in origin. Autopsies have shown the brain of the Neurotypical is typically smaller than that of an autistic individual and may have overdeveloped areas related to social behaviour."

Muskie, 1999, cited in Bogdashina, 2006, p. 88.

Recommended Reading

Here follows a reading list of material that I have found particularly helpful. Some of these are also included in the references to this book and others are not explicitly referred to, but all helped me greatly in learning about Autism.

Articles, Websites and CD-ROMs

Baron-Cohen, S., Wheelwright, S., Skinner, R., Martin, J. & Clubley, E. (2001). The Autism-Spectrum Quotient (AQ): evidence from Asperger Syndrome/high-functioning Autism, males and females, scientists and mathematicians. *Journal of Autism and Developmental Disorders, 31,* 5-17.

The AQ Test can also be found at: http://www.wired.com/wired/archive/9.12/aqtest.html.

Cambridge University Autism Research Centre. *Mind-reading: the interactive guide to emotions (CD-ROM).* London: Jessica Kingsley (2002).

www.jordanseyes.com - website of Ian Jordan, who prescribes tinted lenses to spectrum folk and others, for example, those with dyslexia and dyspraxia.

Jordan, I. (2009). Prosopagnosia: an introduction for eye care providers. *Optometry Today,* 26-28.

www.respectrum.com - help with implementing the GF-CF diet.

Segar, M., (undated). *Coping: A Survival Guide for people with Asperger Syndrome.* http://www-users.cs.york.ac.uk/~alistair/survival/index.html

Books

Attwood, T. (2007). *The Complete Guide to Asperger's Syndrome.* London: Jessica Kingsley.

Bogdashina, O. (2003). *Sensory Perceptual Issues in Autism and Asperger Syndrome.* London: Jessica Kingsley.

Bogdashina, O. (2005). *Communication Issues in Autism and Asperger Syndrome: Do we speak the same language?* London: Jessica Kingsley.

Bogdashina, O. (2006). *Theory of Mind and the Triad of Perspectives on Autism and Asperger Syndrome.* London: Jessica Kingsley.

Edmonds, G. & Worton, D. (2005). *The Asperger Love Guide: A Practical Guide for Adults with Asperger's Syndrome to Seeking, Establishing and Maintaining Successful Relationships.* London: Paul Chapman Publishing.

Edmonds, G. & Worton, D. (2006). *The Asperger Social Guide: How to Relate to Anyone in any Social Situation as an Adult with Asperger's Syndrome.* London: Paul Chapman Publishing.

Edmonds, G. & Worton, D. (2006). *The Asperger Personal Guide: Raising Self-Esteem and Making the Most of Yourself as a Adult with Asperger's Syndrome.* London: Paul Chapman Publishing.

Holliday Willey, L. (1999). *Pretending to be Normal: Living with Asperger Syndrome.* London: Jessica Kingsley.

Holliday Willey, L. (2001). *Asperger Syndrome in the Family: Redefining Normal.* London: Jessica Kingsley.

Jackson, J. (2004). *Multicoloured Mayhem: Parenting the Many Shades of Adolescents and Children with Autism, Asperger Syndrome and AD/HD.* London: Jessica Kingsley.

Recommended Reading

Jackson, L. (2002a). *A User Guide to the GF-CF Diet for Autism, Asperger Syndrome and AD/HD*. London: Jessica Kingsley.

Jackson, L. (2002b). *Freaks, Geeks & Asperger Syndrome*. London: Jessica Kingsley.

Le Breton, M. (2002). *The AiA Gluten and Dairy Free Cookbook*. London: Jessica Kingsley.

Le Breton, M. (2001). *Diet Intervention and Autism: Implementing the Gluten Free and Casein Free Diet for Autistic Children and Adults*. London: Jessica Kingsley.

Lawson, W. (1998). *Life behind Glass: A Personal Account of Autism Spectrum Disorder*. London: Jessica Kingsley.

Lawson, W. (2001). *Understanding and Working With the Spectrum of Autism: An Insider's View*. London: Jessica Kingsley.

Williams, D. (1996). *Autism: An Inside-Out Approach*. London: Jessica Kingsley.

References

Alcántara, J. I., Weisblatt, E. J. L., Moore, B. C. J. & Bolton, P. F. (2004). Speech-in-noise perception in high-functioning individuals with Autism or Asperger's Syndrome. *Journal of Child Psychology and Psychiatry, 45,* 1107-1114.

Allen, D., Evans, C., Hider, A., Hawkins, S., Peckett, H & Morgan, H. (2008). Offending Behaviour in Adults with Asperger Syndrome. *Journal of Autism and other Developmental Disorders, 38* (748-758).

American Psychiatric Association (1994). Diagnostic & Statistical Manual of Mental Disorders, 4th edition, (DSM-IV). Washington DC: American Psychiatric Association.

Ariel, C., N. & Naseef, R. A. (2006). *Voices from the Spectrum: Parents, Grandparents, Siblings, People with Autism and Professionals share their wisdom.* London: Jessica Kingsley.

Attwood, T. (2007). *The Complete Guide to Asperger's Syndrome.* London: Jessica Kingsley.

Barlow, W. (1976). "Mens Sana…" Once More: A Review Essay of The Alexander Technique. *Biofeedback and Self-Regulation, 1,* 241-249.

Baron-Cohen, S., Leslie, A. & Frith, U. (1985). Does the autistic child have a "theory of mind"? *Cognition, 21,* 37-46.

Baron-Cohen, S., O-Riordan, M., Stone, V., Jones, R. & Plaisted, K. (1999). Recognition of Faux Pas by Normally Developing Children and Children with Asperger Syndrome or High-Functioning Autism. *Journal of Autism and Developmental Disorders, 29,* 407-418.

References

Baron-Cohen, S. & Wheelwright, S. (2004). The Empathy Quotient: An Investigation of Adults with Asperger Syndrome or High Functioning Autism, and Normal Sex Differences. *Journal of Autism and Developmental Disorders, 34*, 163-175.

Bloch, M. (2004). *F. M. Alexander: The life of Frederick Matthias, Founder of the Alexander Technique.* London: Little, Brown.

Bogdashina, O. (2003). *Sensory Perceptual Issues in Autism and Asperger Syndrome.* London: Jessica Kingsley.

Bogdashina, O. (2005). *Communication Issues in Autism and Asperger Syndrome: Do we speak the same language?* London: Jessica Kingsley.

Bogdashina, O. (2006). *Theory of Mind and the Triad of Perspectives on Autism and Asperger Syndrome.* London: Jessica Kingsley.

Bowler, D. (1992). "Theory of Mind" in Asperger's Syndrome. *Journal of Child Psychology and Psychiatry, 33*, 877-893.

Dawson, G., & Watling, R. (2000). Interventions to Facilitate Auditory, Visual and Motor Integration in Autism: A Review of the Evidence. *Journal of Autism and Developmental Disorders, 30*, 415-421.

Dennis, M., Lazenby, A.L. & Lockyer, L. (2001). Inferential Language in High-Function Children with Autism. *Journal of Autism and Developmental Disorders, 31*, 47-54.

Dumortier, D., (2002). *From Another Planet: Autism from Within.* Antwerp: Houtekiet.

Dunn, W., Saiter, J., & Rinner, L. (2002). Asperger Syndrome and Sensory Processing: A conceptual Model and Guidance for Intervention Planning. *Focus on Autism and Other Developmental Disabilities, 17*, 172-185.

Edmonds, G. & Beardon, L. (2008). *Asperger Syndrome & Social Relationships*. London: Jessica Kingsley.

Frith, U. (1998). What Autism teaches us about communication. *Logopedics Phoniatrics Vocology, 23,* 51-58.

Frith, U. (1991). *Autism and Asperger Syndrome*. Cambridge: Cambridge University Press.

Frith, U. & Happé, F. (1994a). Autism: beyond "theory of mind". *Cognition, 50,* 115-132.

Frith, U. & Happé, F. (1994b). Language and communication in autistic disorders. *Philosophical Transactions of the Royal Society, 346,* 97-104.

Gelb, M. (1981). *Body Learning: An introduction to the Alexander Technique*. London: Aurum Press Limited.

Green, D., Baird, G., Barnett, A., Henderson, L., Huber, J. & Henderson, S.E. (2002). The severity and nature of motor impairment in Asperger's syndrome: a comparison with Specific Developmental Disorder of Motor Function. *Journal of Child Psychology and Psychiatry, 43,* 655-668.

Hall, K. (2001). *Asperger Syndrome, the Universe and Everything*. London: Jessica Kingsley.

Harrison, J., & Hare, D. J. (2004). Brief Report: Assessment of Sensory Abnormalities in People with Autistic Spectrum Disorders. *Journal of Autism and Developmental Disorders, 34,* 727-730.

Hill, E. & Frith, U. (2003). Understanding Autism: insights from mind and brain. *Philosophical Transactions of the Royal Society, 358,* 281-289.

References

Holliday Willey, L. (1999). *Pretending to be Normal: Living with Asperger Syndrome.* London: Jessica Kingsley.

Holliday Willey, L. (2001). *Asperger Syndrome in the Family: Redefining Normal.* London: Jessica Kingsley.

Howlin, P. (2003). Outcome in High-Functioning Adults with Autism With and Without Early Language Delays: Implications for the Differentiation between Autism and Asperger Syndrome. Humphrey, N. (2008). Including pupils with autistic spectrum disorders in mainstream schools. *Support for Learning, 23,* 41-47.

http://en.wikipedia.org/wiki/Asperger_Syndrome

Iarocci, G., & McDonald, J. (2006). Sensory Integration and the Perceptual Experience of Persons with Autism. *Journal of Autism and Developmental Disorders, 36,* 77-90.

ICD-10. (1994). *International Classification of Diseases (10th edition).* Geneva, Switzerland: World Health Organisation.

Jain, S., Janssen, K. & DeCelle, S. (2004). Alexander Technique and Feldenkrais method: a critical overview. *Phys Med Rehabil Clin N Am, 15,* 811-825.

Knivsberg, A., Reichelt, K., Hoien, T. & Nodland, M. (2003). Effect of a Dietary Intervention on Autistic Behavior. *Focus on Autism and other Developmental Disabilities, 18,* 248-257.

Krebs, J. (2004). The curious naturalist. *Nature, 427,* 293-294.

Jackson, J. (2004). *Multicoloured Mayhem: Parenting the Many Shades of Adolescents and Children with Autism, Asperger Syndrome and AD/HD.* London: Jessica Kingsley.

Jackson, L. (2002a). *A User Guide to the GF-CF Diet for Autism, Asperger Syndrome and AD/HD*. London: Jessica Kingsley.

Jackson, L. (2002b). *Freaks, Geeks & Asperger Syndrome*. London: Jessica Kingsley.

Jain, S., Janssen, K. & DeCelle, S. (2004). Alexander Technique and Feldenkrais method: a critical overview. *Physical Medicine and Rehabiltation clinics of North America, 15*, 811-825.

Jansson-Verkasalo, E., Ceponiene, R., Kielinen, M., Suominen, K., Jantti, V., Linna, S.L., Moilanen, I. & Naatanen, R. (2003). Deficient auditory processing in children with Asperger Syndrome, as indexed by event-related potentials. *Neuroscience Letters, 338*, 197-200.

Jolliffe, T. & Baron-Cohen, S. (1999). A test of central coherence theory: linguistic processing in high-functioning adults with Autism or Asperger Syndrome: is local coherence impaired? *Cognition, 71*, 149-185.

Jordan, I. (2009). Prosopagnosia: an introduction for eye care providers. *Optometry Today*, 26-28.

Kanner, L. (1943) Autistic disturbances of affective contact. *Nervous Child, 2*, 217-250.

Lawson, W. (2001). *Understanding and Working With the Spectrum of Autism: An Insider's View*. London: Jessica Kingsley.

Le Breton, M. (2002). *The AiA Gluten & Dairy Free Cookbook*. London: Jessica Kingsley.

References

Martin, I. & McDonald, S. (2004). An Exploration of Causes of Non-Literal Language Problems in Individuals with Asperger Syndrome. *Journal of Autism and Developmental Disorders, 34,* 311-328.

Millward, C., Ferriter, M., Calver, S. & Connell-Jones, G. (2004). Gluten- and casein-free diets for autistic spectrum disorder. *Cochrane Database of Systematic Reviews, 2,* 1-12.

Minshew, N. J., Sung, K., Jones, B. L. & Furman, J. M., (2004). Underdevelopment of the postural control system in Autism. *Neurology, 63,* 2056-2061.

Miyahara, M., Tsujii, M., Hori, M., Nakanishi, K., Kageyama, H., & Sugiyama, T., (1997). Brief Report: Motor Incoordination in Children with Asperger Syndrome and Learning Disabilities. *Journal of Autism and Developmental Disorders, 27,* 595-603.

Molloy, C., Dietrich, K. & Bhattacharya, A. (2003). Postural Stability in Children with Autism Spectrum Disorder. *Journal of Autism and Developmental Disorders, 33,* 643-652.

Murray, D., Lesser, M. & Lawson, W. (2005). Attention, monotropism and the diagnostic criteria for Autism. *Autism, 9,* 139-156.

Norbury, C.F. & Bishop, D.V.M. (2002). Inferential processing and story recall in children with communication problems: a comparison of specific language impairment, pragmatic language impairment and high-functioning Autism. *International Journal of Language & Communication Disorders, 37,* 227-251.

O'Conner, K., Hamm, J.P. & Kirk, I.J. (2007). Neurophysiological responses to face, facial regions and objects in adults with Asperger's Syndrome: An ERP investigation. *International Journal of Psychophysiology, 63,* 283-293.

Quigley, E. M. M. & Hurley, D. (2000). Autism and the Gastrointestinal Tract. *AJG, 95,* 2154-2155.

Schultz, R. T., Gauthier, I., Klin, A., Fulbright, R.K., Anderson, A.W., Volkmar, F., Skudlarski, P., Lacadie, C., Cohen, D.J. & Gore, J.C. (2000). Abnormal Ventral Temporal Cortical Activity During Face Discrimination Among Individuals With Autism and Asperger Syndrome. *Arch Gen Psychiatry, 57,* 331-340.

Scottish Intercollegiate Guidelines Network (2007). *Assessment, diagnosis and clinical interventions for children and young people with Autism spectrum disorders: A national clinical guideline.* Edinburgh: Author.

Segar, M., (undated). *Coping: A Survival Guide for people with Asperger Syndrome.* http://www-users.cs.york.ac.uk/~alistair/survival/index.html

Shelly, S. (2004). *Women from another planet? Feminism and AC awareness.* A presentation at Autreat 2004.

Smukler, D. (2005). Unauthorized Minds: How "Theory of Mind" Theory Misrepresents Autism. *Mental Retardation, 43,* 11-24.

Tinbergen, N. (1973). Ethology and Stress Diseases: Nobel Lecture, 12 December 1973. *Physiology or Medicine,* 113-130.

The National Autistic Society (2009). Dear friends (letter by Neil). *Asperger United, October 2009,* 10-11.

Wakefield, A. J., Puleston, J. M., Montgomery, S. M., Anthony, A., O'Leary, J. J. & Murch, S., H. (2002). Review article: the concept of entero-colonic encephalopathy, Autism and opioid receptor ligands. *Aliment Parmacol Ther, 16,* 663-674.

References

Whiteley, P., Rodgers, J., Savery, D. & Shattock, P (1999). A gluten-free diet as an intervention for Autism and associated spectrum disorders: preliminary findings. *Autism, 3*, 45-65.

Williams, D. (1996). *Autism: An Inside-Out Approach.* London: Jessica Kingsley.

Williams, D. (1998). *Autism and Sensing: The Unlost Instinct.* London: Jessica Kingsley.

Wing, L. (1996). *The Autistic Spectrum: a guide for parents and professionals.* London: Constable.

Wing, L. (1997). The History of Ideas on Autism: Legends, Myths and Reality. *Autism, 1*, 13-23.

Wing, L. (2004). The spectrum of autistic disorders. *Hospital Medicine, 65*, 542-545.